KITCHEN YOGA
UNDERSTANDING FOOD

KITCHEN YOGA
UNDERSTANDING FOOD

by
MARGARET DAVIDSON

illustrated by
MAIJA ROBINSON

DEDICATION

For Catherine who taught me to listen,
and for the adorable "Peanut"

ISBN 0-9551962-0-5

Design and typesetting by www.simprimstudio.com

Printed and bound in Great Britain by
Martins the Printers Limited, Sea View Works, Spittal, Berwick-upon-Tweed
www.martins-the-printers.com

Published by Peanut Productions in 2006
© Margaret Davidson 2006

The authors assert their moral right to be identified as
the authors of this work.

All rights reserved.
No part of this publication may be reproduced,
stored in a retrieval system, or transmitted, in any form or by any means,
electronic, mechanical, photocopying, recording or otherwise,
without the prior permission of the publisher.

ACKNOWLEDGMENTS

I would like to thank my Yoga-Weekend students for actively encouraging me to write a book that had resided in my head the better part of thirty years.

My friend and co-author Maija for her patience, generosity and time spent so lovingly illustrating the text; her husband, Simon, for all his contributory inputs; John, for the photographs – and the months spent proof-reading and editing the text!

Joan Deitch, my agent at Pollinger's for her tireless endeavours on my behalf, her unwavering support and much valued friendship; and everyone at Pollinger's who were involved at some stage in this publication.

I owe a special debt of gratitude to my husband and children for enduring years of experimentation with ingredients and healthcare that, at the time, were far from main-stream.

And last, but not least, all those who have influenced my thinking, a list too long to mention everyone personally but, on the nutritional front, especially the philosophers and practitioners: Rudolph Ballantine M.D., Anne- Marie Colbin, Jacob Liebermann and Michio Kushi; the late Rudolph Steiner and, in particular, his adherent and fellow scientific philosopher, Rudolph Hauschka.

My yoga teachers and friends: John Stirk F.R.C.O, Carrie Tuke and Sandra Sabatini – for sharing themselves as much as their insights and expertise; Val Thorman for scrutinising the yoga section. And finally, with profound reverence and gratitude, the late Jiddhu Krishnamurti whose philosophy and writings underpin my own practice and inspire my life.

There are hundreds of texts, treatises and yoga books and possibly many hundreds more on cookery, so why another one? Neither one nor the other, Kitchen Yoga is a synthesis designed to re-awaken and nourish an innate human response to natural foods by blending practicalities with philosophy.

Because yoga is ubiquitous it cannot be captured, codified or described adequately in words. Any attempt to do so could only ever be a partial explanation or description of the single reality, the one truth that comprises wholeness. Thus, road-building yoga, astrophysics yoga, fishing yoga, dancing yoga – each, in its own way, is as valid as kitchen yoga. That I have chosen the kitchen as a context derives solely out of a personal fascination with our complex inter-relationship with our basic support system: food. The emphasis in Kitchen Yoga is as much about our attitudes and relationship to food, as about what we eat or how we cook.

INTRODUCTION

I was born to a mother who would not cook. She demonstrated a disdain for food in general and mealtimes in particular. She would sigh, frequently, "If only someone would invent a pill....!" Her implication being that all the time and energy wasted on eating could be spent on more worthwhile pursuits such as sewing or amateur dramatics.

Fortunately we lived in Africa where a cook came with the job but when independence was declared and we were obliged to return to the UK, having a mother who refused to cook could have become a liability. You might say it was a defining moment. In the event my father stepped into the breach; and I have cooked from the age of twelve.

All our African cooks relied on previous experience and an instinct for ingredients that allowed them to consistently produce excellent meals. I must have absorbed their intuitive, practical approach to cooking because it was our several African cooks who fuelled an early culinary curiosity in me.

In the absence of TV and other latter-day distractions I became a fixture in the kitchen, fascinated by the alchemy of food, the seemingly miraculous transformation of raw ingredients into a set piece, the limitless combinations of individual substances and colours translating into something inconceivable to the uninitiated. Ice-cream, curry or cake, were nothing less than miracles, and Mpishi was "god". To this day I can remember his guiding hand directing my first attempt at cake-making. It was a two-coloured sponge and involved whisking egg whites – an opaque slop of substance whipped into a voluminous fluffy cloud. That was awesome and I was captivated.

I am aware that not everyone shares my passion for cooking. I doubt my mother's viewpoint is unique although, throughout the 1950s, most mothers would have expected to cook. For the modern woman / man technology offers tantalising alternatives to long hours spent in a kitchen. Most modern women expect to spend a good part of their lives outside the home. They have careers and the pre-packed meal and takeaway are a godsend. Our schools teach home-craft with a bias towards technology in place of old-fashioned domestic science.

This is not to criticise modern practice but to question whether the cost of liberation from the domestic sink has come at an extortionate price, depriving some individuals of an innately creative outlet. Not knowing where to start, lacking the confidence to try, or too stressed-out and exhausted through "real" work, it is hardly surprising cooking is frequently considered a chore rather than a pleasure. Paradoxically, cookery programmes are favourite TV viewing. So, instead of an engaging activity, cooking has been turned into the equivalent of a spectator sport. Besides, good restaurants abound and pubs serve food all day. Why compete in a world of experts?

In writing KITCHEN YOGA I am attempting to redress an imbalance rather than turn the clock back to some mythical "golden age". It is intended for both those who love to cook and those who don't but are willing to "give it a go". Rather than chapters, I have divided the text into sections for easy reference, that allow for dipping in and out and negating a necessity to read the book from cover to cover.

Throughout the 13 years I taught wholefood cookery and nutrition on Tyneside and in Northumberland I encouraged students to trust their senses and experiment with ingredients, often without recourse to a recipe. The results were rewarding, sometimes amazing, and if nothing else made for self-confidence. In KITCHEN YOGA I have dispensed with calories; measurements are sometimes approximate because I tend to rely on instinct, common sense and above all a "feel" for the food I want to translate into a meal. Colour, shape, texture, combinations, location and production are as important for me as linear accuracy.

The philosophical or yoga aspect of the book is woven as a thread throughout the text and has less to do with exercises inviting the body to assume difficult (or well-nigh impossible) positions – although a few simple routines are offered in a dedicated section – than attitude, awareness and intention. The "yoga" is food for the mind, extending an invitation to be mindful, of our self, and of our relationship with others. Developing an awareness of an on-going relationship with food allows us to become more deeply committed to truly feeding and nourishing ourselves.

Yoga informs balance and dietary balance is as much a part of the practice as postures, movement or meditation. I have aimed for balance on several levels. Preparing the body for food is, I believe, as important as preparing food for the body. In compiling this book I have striven for common sense whilst borrowing from the accumulated knowledge and wisdom of minds more scholarly and enlightened than my own. I remain indebted to the many teachers whom I have never personally met, who have inspired me through their writings; and to those who have shared their practical experience, as well as their generosity of spirit, in demonstrating unfailing patience with a child who was forever asking "Why?"

I have divided the book into sections for easy reference.

Menus are colour-coded:

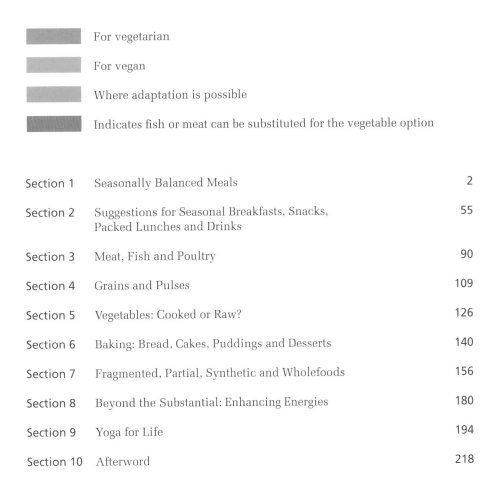

For vegetarian

For vegan

Where adaptation is possible

Indicates fish or meat can be substituted for the vegetable option

HOW TO USE THIS BOOK

SECTION ONE
Seasonally balanced meals

This covers three-course meals inspired by a small group of yoga students and teachers who meet once a month to practice in an idyllic rural setting in North Northumberland.

The intention is to develop personal and communal growth with attention to our environment and the five physical senses. Weather permitting, we spend time walking meditatively experiencing the sense of touch, sight, hearing and smell. Taste is reflected in lunch, which comprises organic produce wherever possible. Fresh ingredients are prepared and cooked from scratch. The meals are cooked by gas but can as easily be cooked by electricity. Microwaves are excluded. The menus are for eight but are easily adaptable for fewer servings.

September reflects Keats' "season of mists and mellow fruitfulness", shortening days, luminous milky moons, and the rituals of harvest suppers. The latter demonstrate not only gratitude for Nature's bounty but a keen appreciation of our connections with something bigger than our Self.

The season begins with fruition: the manifestation of Nature's summery labours, which we harvest, store and consume through the long lean months of winter. Or at least we used to prior to the wonders of modern technology that have dispensed with the uncertainties of an irregular food supply. Nowadays we reap the advantages of a world shrink-wrapped to the size of a global village: not only can we eat what we like, when we like and as often as we like, the very idea of the food supply being limited seems preposterous. And that is not to be decried, although it may be worth remembering only a generation or two ago availability was reduced to the home market, and some people maintain that we were healthier as a result.

A full larder equates with comfort and security but if prolonged, will inevitably lead to loss of appetite as the pendulum swings towards its opposite polarity.

In the animal kingdom the keenness of hunger sharpens instinct for survival. For the most part we have tamed our physical environment, so the urgency of obtaining the next meal has been removed and our instincts have dulled into habit. This has enabled us to engage our mental faculties more fully. In respect of our food the energy expended is mostly mental: deciding where and when to go to the supermarket, selecting from an almost unlimited range of produce and delivering it home brings dinner onto the table. The most physically demanding aspect of this process is probably unloading the shopping trolley into the car boot, taking it out again at the other end and distributing it around the kitchen shelves and refrigerator/freezer. Nothing comparable with actually digging the ground and tending the soil and its produce.

When the weekly supermarket trip becomes a repetitive chore we become bored. Our restless minds demand diversity and fascination with our mental capabilities has led us to manipulate foods to a degree that all too frequently renders them unrecognisable from their original basic state.

Somewhere along this road our minds have separated out from our bodies: the one wants excitement and titillation, the other craves nourishment. These cravings result in over-consumption and under-nourishment which then lead to crash dieting, food fads, allergies and addictions not to mention the other forms of torture we mentally inflict upon the body in an attempt to silence its clamour. We will either indulge it or deny it. Anything but feed it!

To experience wholeness again, to heal, to allow mind and body to reintegrate, means eating wholesome foods rather than fragmented manipulated substances that masquerade as foods. Systemically we are not designed to absorb and metabolise a cocktail of chemicals; we are designed to interact with what the Earth yields up out of its own wisdom.

A system bigger than our own, of which we are a part, requires that we eat mostly what is available seasonally whilst paying attention to our own rhythms. We breathe: we exhale and we inhale and in between these two polarities there is a pause. We need to exercise this pause between meal times. We need to eat at regular intervals instead of grazing on the hoof like overfed wildebeest. Nor are we ruminants. Yet walk down any high street and mouths are to be observed in perpetual motion, if not processing food then masticating gum.

We experience neither emptiness, nor the satisfaction of fullness that accrues from total emptiness because we are forever topping up. We have no real appetite anymore. We settle for over-salted and over-sweetened concoctions and rarely experience the delight of sharp, sour or bitter tastes. Without astringency we become sluggish, not just physically but mentally as well. So much of what we ascribe to stress is mental lethargy rather than a natural tiredness derived from sustained physical activity. We can, however, reverse this trend if we choose.

Centrally heated homes and sedentary lifestyles mean we do not need to consume the quantities of food our grandparents needed for fuel and warmth.

Preparing food from scratch rather than putting a ready-meal in the microwave may be time-consuming but we might benefit from slowing down to some extent; and gadget wizardry allows kitchen chores to be performed within a fraction of the time required in Grandma's day.

Washing and chopping vegetables done with attention is meditation. Paying attention is the key to any successful outcome: we are naturally inventive so our creativity is developed and what may start out as a chore soon becomes a pleasure. Success breeds success.

The intrinsic of food preparation cannot be measured linearly but many ancient texts allude to the importance of placing our own energy into the food if our families are to be adequately nourished. "Never cook when in a bad mood because it will affect the outcome of the meal" is an adage I have followed ever since I gave my husband indigestion through baking bread when in a rush and a sour temper.

I have discovered real power exists in the kitchen. We influence our families' lives not only by what we provide but also by how we provide it. Sitting down and eating together (without the intrusion of the television), even for one daily meal, encourages healthy communication amongst families.

This is not a question of believing me but of trying it and finding out whether or not it is true for you. The word community is a derivative of communication after all.

With Nature as our foremost guide and all the benefits of technology at our disposal we can confidently experiment. Electricity may have artificially extended our day, yet we know there is a different feel to a spring day as opposed to a winter one.

Autumn is the beginning of a withdrawal, it is a time for introspection and contemplation; a mourning for the passing year, a concentration or gathering in of information; it is wisdom as opposed to learning.

I find I am less inclined to relish salads when there is a nip of frost in the air; I'd rather drink hot blackcurrant juice than chilled orange which is more expansive; I want thick soups rather than consommé which is too thin; and I relish root vegetables in preference to raw celery.

I want hearty roasts, baked potatoes and boiled vegetables in preference to steamed ones unless, in the case of celery, the vegetable is not robust enough to warrant boiling. This does not mean I do not eat raw foods during the colder seasons, just that I eat more cooked and concentrated foods at these times. My body appreciates the extra warmth to balance the rawness of the weather and retains its reserves of energy for warding off those seasonal cold and 'flu bugs.

So, let's relax and begin……..

Menu serves 8

Baked Avocados with Red Pepper Purée
Green Salad of Lambs' Lettuce, Rocket and Watercress
Homemade Malted Bread with organic butter/olive oil
Leek Tarte
Red Cabbage
Apricot Fluff

Because I work outside home organising my time is essential. I start with the bread as the other components of the meal can be fitted around the risings. For this menu, however, both bread and sweet can be made the day before.

MALTED BREAD (Section Six – Bread: Granary baps)

BAKED AVOCADOS

4 large firm, ripe avocados

2 large red peppers roughly chopped

4 large unpeeled cloves garlic

1 medium–large onion

70 gm thinly sliced and chopped button mushrooms

2 tbs virgin olive oil / organic sunflower oil

1 tbs lemon juice

Sea salt and pepper

1 tsp dried Italian herbs or equivalent or
1 tbs mixed chopped fresh herbs e.g. parsley, rosemary, basil, chervil, marjoram and thyme.

100 gm grated Gruyere cheese

8 florets of fresh parsley for garnish (leave some of the stalk intact because it is the properties in the stalk that assist the uptake of the valuable iron – and encourage your guests to eat the garnish rather than set it aside!)

Sprinkling of dried chilli (optional)

Place the garlic and chopped peppers in a pan, cover with boiling water and simmer, covered, for approximately 10 minutes. Drain.

Peel the garlic and place this, the peppers and the lemon juice in a liquidiser and blend. Set aside.

Peel and finely chop the onion and, using a fry pan, soften in the oil, taking care not to brown.

Add the sliced, chopped mushrooms, the herbs and seasoning to taste and cook for a few minutes until the mushrooms are soft. Turn off the heat.

Then mix in the pepper and garlic puree, scraping out the blender with a spatula.

Halve and pit the avocados, and slice off a thin piece of the surface skin underneath so that the fruit will sit on a flat surface without rolling.

Fill with pepper and mushroom mixture, covering the surface as well as the hollow.

Sprinkle with the grated cheese and, optionally, the chilli.

Organise the fruits on an oiled baking tray and bake in the centre of the oven (Gas 5 / 190 C) for approximately 10–15 minutes.

To serve, arrange in a pre-heated oven-proof dish and top with the parsley. I like to use brown or orange earthenware flat dishes to balance the green avocado and red and green topping.

To complement the dish I serve up a large green salad of lambs' lettuce and mixed leaves of watercress and rocket in a large glass bowl so that the colour contrast is effective. A few minutes prior to dishing up I scatter the salad lightly with a little sea salt and drizzle with olive oil, stirring lightly with wooden salad servers.

And I cut the bread in chunks, unless serving it as bread rolls, and place these in a basket or wooden bowl, to complete the picture. Serve with a good quality creamy organic butter.

LEEK TARTE

Autumn leeks are deliciously succulent so I always use plenty whether as a main dish or a side vegetable.

A deep serving dish for 8 lined with a rich shortcrust pastry – 350 gm flour to 175 gm butter / shortening should suffice. I prefer SR (self-raising) to plain flour and I sift it twice into a large mixing bowl to ensure a good air supply. Lightly rub in the shortening with your fingertips until the mixture resembles fine breadcrumbs. (I always use butter but lard is good too unless you are vegetarian). Then slowly add sufficient iced water to roughly mix the crumbs together with a spatula. Gather up the mixture with your fingertips and work into a soft pliable ball.

For the filling

6–8 slender young leeks about 2.5 cm diameter and 20–25 cm length, thoroughly cleaned

A little ghee or olive oil in which to sweat the leeks

250 gm grated Gruyere cheese

200 ml organic crème fraîche

2 heaped tbs fresh chopped parsley

Sea salt and pepper and nutmeg to taste

Note: Nutmeg is toxic in large amounts. ¼ tsp is adequate for this dish.

Handy Hint: To chop parsley efficiently push it into a mug and scissor it. The task is completed in seconds.

Lemon juice added to the water tends to give the pastry a nice crisp texture. If you overdo the water just a little it is possible to salvage the disaster by quickly adding more flour and blending well.

Leave the pastry to rest for a few minutes. Then roll out on a floured surface to a size larger than the dish, trim the edges with a sharp knife leaving sufficient for shrinkage to take place. Chill in the fridge or leave in a cool place whilst preparing the filling.

Slice the leeks lengthways along the direction of growth and ensure you slice away from you so that your energy is directed into the food. Then finely chop and sweat them in a little ghee or olive oil for a few minutes just to take off the rawness but not so long that they become tender. Alternatively, if you are trying to reduce your fat intake, you can blanch them and then drain.

In a bowl mix the finely chopped leeks, parsley, seasoning and cheese with the crème fraîche. Pour into the pastry crust and bake in the centre of a hot oven (Gas 6 / 200 C) for 40 – 45 minutes. The leeks need to be thoroughly cooked but check that they are not browning after 30 mins; if necessary turn down the heat. Scatter some parsley sprigs over the top just prior to serving.

For a richer tart you can blend a raw egg into the mixture prior to cooking.

This will produce a firmer, set filling.

If you don't like crème fraîche use whipping cream.

In summer I serve this tarte warm with a large mixed salad. In the Autumn I find it marries well with red cabbage as an accompaniment and in winter I like to use mashed butternut squash sprinkled with roasted cashews.

In a large fry pan (with lid) sweat the garlic and onion in the ghee/oil over a medium to low flame/heat. Remove the lid, add the cabbage and coat well with the melted ghee. Add the apple, stirring continuously. Season and sprinkle on the sugar and vinegar. Stir in the raisins and the cinnamon. Cover with a well fitting lid and turn the heat down to its lowest setting. Cook for 10–15 minutes. The cabbage needs to be tender but not collapsed. Check that the mixture does not dry out or it will burn. Add a little hot water from time to time if necessary, and check the flavour. If it is too sharp for your taste add a little more sugar, if too sweet add extra vinegar.

Turn out into a pre-heated serving dish and keep warm until required.

Sometimes I add a knob of butter just before serving – it gives a gloss.

This dish can be reheated but it will not taste quite the same as served up fresh from the pan.

RED CABBAGE

1 whole small red cabbage or a section of a large one, sliced and shredded

1 large onion sliced and finely chopped

2–4 cloves garlic (optional), finely chopped

2 medium sweet red eating apples, peeled, cored and roughly quartered

1–2 tbs of cider or raspberry vinegar

1 scant handful raisins

1 – 2 dsp cinnamon

1 large tbs Demerara sugar

Salt and pepper to taste

1 generous tbs ghee or 2 tbs olive oil

A little water

APRICOT FLUFF

250 gm dried apricots washed and soaked overnight

450 gm live bio yoghurt

3–4 tbs clear organic honey

200 ml whipping cream lightly whipped to a firm but dropping consistency (optional)

8 halved walnuts or blanched almonds/ cherries / angelica for decoration

Drain the apricots and retain the liquid.

Blend the apricots in a food blender and scoop the pulp into a mixing bowl. If there is difficulty in getting out all the fruit add a small amount of the retained liquid and whizz round in the blender, pour this onto the fruit and mix thoroughly with a spatula. Stir in the yoghurt carefully and mix well. Then add sufficient honey to sweeten according to your taste.

Divide into 8 glass dishes and decorate with the cream and choice of topping. The cream can be omitted. Angelica and cherries contrast fittingly with the apricot colour. And when I made this for my children I would sometimes sprinkle grated chocolate (sparingly!) over the top.

For a quick version substitute the dried apricots with 2 jars "Whole Earth" unsweetened apricot jam, dispense with the blending and simply soften using a wooden spoon before adding the rest of the ingredients. Check for sweetness; you may find you require less honey.

Avocado Hummus and fresh white Bread Rolls / Toast
Mixed Bean Casserole and Creamed Spinach
Apple and Orange Crumble with Crème Fraîche / Custard

Drain the chickpeas and bring to the boil in a pan of fresh water. Cover with a lid and simmer until soft. This takes about ½ hr – it often depends on how old the chickpeas are. Never cook legumes (peas and beans) with salt as it toughens them. Drain the chickpeas retaining the liquid.

Then place in a blender or food processor with the remaining ingredients and sufficient chickpea liquid required for the puree to become the consistency of creamy mashed potatoes. It needs to be soft and firm, not sloppy. Sometimes no extra liquid is required at all. Check the taste – you may want to sharpen the flavour with extra lemon juice or add a little more tahini if you really enjoy the taste of sesame. Scrape out into a deep bowl. I use a red bowl in the cooler months, a cobalt blue one in the summer. Place this in the centre of a tray scattered with salad leaves and serve with warm toast or fresh bread rolls. Dispense with butter – it is superfluous and will mask the flavour of the hummus.

BREAD ROLLS (Section 6)

AVOCADO HUMMUS

200 gm dried chickpeas soaked overnight

4 cloves garlic crushed

4 tbs fresh lemon juice

200 ml light tahini

1 tsp salt

2–4 tbs olive oil

Liquid from *cooked* chickpeas

2 large avocados or 3 small ones pitted, peeled and roughly chopped

These amounts make a generous quantity and any leftover can be frozen without impairment to the flavour. Overall, I am disinclined to freeze foods, preferring to eat them fresh, but sometimes it is useful to have something ready to hand for when unexpected visitors turn up, or you are busy and want an instant starter so that you can tend to a more intricate main course or dessert without becoming flustered.

Hummus is highly nutritious, rich in vitamins and minerals, unsaturated fats and provides a complete protein meal for vegans and vegetarians.

Chickpeas, also known as garbanzos, contain more vitamin C and double the amount of iron than most legumes and in North Africa dried chickpeas, are ground into flour to form the essential part of couscous.

MIXED VEGETABLE CASSEROLE

For the casserole

500 gm cooked beans

1–2 tbs ghee or olive oil (ghee imparts a richer flavour)

2 tsp black onion seeds

I large onion chopped

1–2 cloves garlic (optional)

Piece of peeled finely chopped root ginger (about the size of the first thumb joint)

1–2 medium-large carrots cut lengthways according to direction of growth and then sliced diagonally into small pieces

½ medium-sized butternut squash peeled and cubed

2 sweet potatoes peeled and cubed

1 courgette roughly chopped

1–2 leeks prepared like the carrots

1 cooked organic sweet corn hulled

1–2 red peppers de-seeded and chopped

1 cupful frozen peas and / or broad beans

1 small head blanched broccoli / cauliflower broken up into florets

1 tin organic chopped tomatoes and half as much water

Some small cooked potatoes (optional)

Spices and Seasoning:

1 tsp lemon juice

1 bay leaf

Pinch mixed herbs

1 tbs Demerara sugar

1 tsp cinnamon

Small cup fresh, chopped parsley for garnish

Pinch cloves

Sea salt and pepper

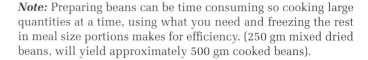

Note: Preparing beans can be time consuming so cooking large quantities at a time, using what you need and freezing the rest in meal size portions makes for efficiency. (250 gm mixed dried beans, will yield approximately 500 gm cooked beans).

Select a colourful blend: red kidney, butter beans, mung, flageolets pintos, blackeyed, soya. Buy organic where possible.

Soak these in a large bowl with a generous covering of cold water overnight. Drain, rinse and bring to the boil in a large pan of fresh water. Allow a brisk boil for at least 10 minutes.

Skim off the froth (scum), cover with the pan lid and simmer until soft. This can take from 30–40 minutes.

For the casserole I use a large heavy-based wok with a lid.

Heat ½ the ghee or oil and add the mustard seed. Cover with the pan lid to prevent them scattering all over the kitchen as they explode. Turn off the heat as soon as the seeds start spitting to ensure the fat does not burn. Wait until they quieten before turning the heat back on low. Add the rest of the ghee or oil, the garlic, ginger and onions. Stir well until the vegetables soften.

Gradually add (stirring to coat well with the fat) the carrots, squash, sweet potato, courgette, leeks, and peppers. Cover for a few minutes and turn down the heat to allow the vegetables to cook in their own moisture.

Then add the chopped tomatoes, sweet corn, beans, spices and seasonings. Stir well; adding sufficient water from the tomato can to ensure a good supply of liquid. Add more water if necessary.

Add the frozen vegetables, the broccoli or cauliflower, and the cooked potatoes (option). Bring back to the boil and check the flavour. If necessary adjust seasoning. Cover with the lid and turn the heat down to the lowest setting. Simmer for ½ hour for all the flavours to be absorbed.

Turn out into a deep pre-heated casserole bowl and sprinkle with chopped fresh parsley. I use an Alasdair Hardie stoneware bowl because I love his earth colours and the texture of the pot lends itself to the heartiness of the casserole: the container and the food balance each other. It reminds me of a saying attributed to the Zen tradition:

Clay is shaped into a pot
But it is the emptiness inside
that holds whatever we want.

This casserole can be served with chunks of bread or plain, boiled rice. It can also be curried using a small jar of curried paste in place of some of the spices.

For an even heartier meal you can add dumplings made with 250 gm SR flour and 125 gm butter/vegetarian suet together with ½ tsp salt rubbed to a consistency of fine breadcrumbs and mixed to a stiff dough with cold water. Divide into small balls and add to the casserole at the point where the last vegetables have been included and cook for 30 minutes.

CREAMED SPINACH

Thoroughly wash 1 kg spinach and steam for 10–15 minutes. Scoop out into a pre-warmed serving bowl; press out and strain any residue liquid, reserving this for stock. Then blend in 1 small carton crème fraîche or ½ small carton whipping cream. Grate a little nutmeg over the top prior to serving (optional).

APPLE & ORANGE CRUMBLE

For the crumble

250 gm organic white SR flour (use wholemeal for a fuller texture)

As an alternative you can substitute 50 gm flour with 2 tbs rolled oats

125 gm organic butter

2 tbs fine natural cane sugar

Using your fingertips rub in the butter with the flour until mixture resembles fine breadcrumbs. Then stir in the sugar.

Fill an oven-proof pie dish up to $^2/_3{}^{rds}$ with pre-cooked sweetened apple into which you have stirred 1 large tbs dark thick-cut marmalade.

Sprinkle on the topping to cover generously. Any left over can be frozen.

Bake in a hot oven (Gas 6 / 200 C) for approximately 30 minutes. Check after 20 minutes and if necessary turn down the heat to prevent browning. I like a pale vanilla coloured crumble but you may prefer a more golden version. Keep warm until required.

Make custard according to directions for **CUSTARD CREAM** (Section One –MARCH: Dessert)

This makes a fairly hearty meal. Unless your guests insist upon coffee, you might like to offer a fruit or green tea to finish off.

If you want to remain caffeine-free and also give your kidneys a tonic you could try Dandelion Coffee.

Spinach Soup
Bulgur Wheat Pilaff
Cream Baked Potatoes
Crème Caramel or Bread and Butter Pudding

Prepare the vegetables. Sweat the onion, garlic, celery, carrot, leek, mushrooms and butternut in heated fat / oil in a large, heavy-based pan with a well-fitting lid.

Add the spinach and water. Bring to the boil and then turn down to simmer with the lid on until cooked (approximately 15–20 mins). Add the potatoes, milk (if using), bouillon powder and seasoning and simmer for a further 5 minutes. Check and increase the liquid with more water if necessary. Turn off the heat and allow to cool prior to blending in a liquidiser. Reheat adding half the cream. Pour into a warmed, large tureen and swirl the rest of the cream over the top prior to serving.

*If using Soya milk add it at point of blending to prevent curdling.

I find the cream definitely enhances the flavour of this soup.

I used to make croutons to go with it rather than bread rolls. Since Phileas Fogg arrived on the scene I've used Mignons Morceaux instead.

SPINACH SOUP

1 large onion finely chopped

2 cloves garlic peeled and finely chopped

125 gm mushrooms wiped and finely sliced

1 stick celery finely chopped

1 large leek cut and sliced into small pieces.

500 gm spinach

1 large carrot thinly sliced or shredded

1 small butternut squash peeled, de-seeded and cubed

3–4 small cooked potatoes cubed

1 tbs ghee / 2 tbs olive oil

800 ml cold water / 400 ml each water and milk / Soya milk*

2 heaped tsp vegetable bouillon powder (2 meat / chicken stock cubes for meat eaters)

Sea salt and pepper

Small carton of cream (optional)

BULGUR WHEAT PILAFF

This is a highly versatile nutritious dish that can be adapted not only for meat eaters but seasonally. It is also quickly prepared and cooked within half an hour.

Sweat in a little olive oil or 1 good tbs ghee a variety of fresh seasonal vegetables. Add 200 gm bulghur wheat and 500 ml water together with 2 tsp vegetable bouillon powder. Stir well, bring to the boil, cover with a well fitting lid and simmer until the bulghur

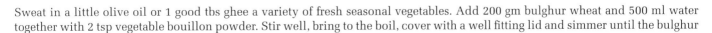

wheat has absorbed the liquid – approximately 15 minutes. Check the seasoning and add some sea salt if required. If this is to be a non-vegetarian dish then add smoked fish or some cubed pieces of pre-cooked pork or chicken at the point where water is being added to the vegetables. For 8 people I would allow 500 gm meat or fish.

As I am serving this in November I use 1–2 cloves garlic, an onion, leeks, carrot, a piece of swede, parsnip, and butternut as a base. I also incorporate some cooked, de-husked organic sweet corn, a tin of organic chopped tomatoes, beetroot, broccoli and cauliflower. Vegetables I omit at all times are kale, sprouts and all varieties of cabbage because they impart too strong a flavour.

In the Spring I would omit the majority of roots in favour of celery, sweet peppers, courgette, sweet potato and aubergine.

In Summer I serve it cold or warm as a salad, using onions, garlic and celery as the base. Then, once the pilaff has cooked and cooled a little I go wild with chopped rocket, cooked peas and green beans, olives, red and yellow bell peppers, fresh, chopped tomato rather than tinned. I add some fresh lemon juice and a little olive oil to gloss it, and lots of ground black pepper. It makes plenty for 8 people and will save in the fridge for a couple of days.

For vegetarians I add cubes of feta cheese, and for non-vegetarians it takes well to fish or chicken. So if you have had roast chicken on Sunday you can use the cold left over chopped into small pieces.

Sauce to accompany the hot vegan / vegetarian pilaff

Fry in a little olive oil 1 crushed clove garlic and 1 finely chopped onion. Add 1½ cups tomato juice, 1/3 cup smooth or crunchy organic peanut butter (depending on whether you prefer a smooth or chewy consistency) diluted with a little warm water. Season with sea salt. Adjust the thickening adding a little more tomato juice or peanut butter as required.

Fresh tuna fish works well, particularly with olives and tomatoes for a Mediterranean flavour. I like to use smoked fish that has not been dyed; cod loin is delicious.

CREAM BAKED POTATOES

Butter a pie or flan dish and ¾ fill with thinly sliced peeled potatoes that have been well rinsed in a colander and placed in a clean tea towel to absorb most of the water. Season with sea salt and pepper and dot each layer with butter.

I find Red Desiree potatoes particularly suitable for this dish because they are waxy in texture and in holding their own they balance the rich overtures of the cream, but really any variety (except for those that turn floury if boiled) will be fine.

Pour a carton of single or whipping cream over the potatoes: 200 ml for 4 people, 400 ml for 8. The cream needs to be almost level with the top layer of potato – if it isn't then top up with organic whole milk. If you like garlic crush one or two cloves into the cream before pouring.

Grate nutmeg sparingly over the top and cover the dish with a lid or foil. Bake for 1 ½–2 hours (Gas 3 / 170 C) or until the potatoes feel tender to the point of a knife.

Scatter sprigs of parsley over the top prior to serving. As an alternative garnish use shavings of fresh parmesan cheese

For 8 people I would allow at least 1.5 kg of peeled potatoes. Vegans can adapt this dish by layering the potatoes alternately with sliced onions and using stock or water in place of milk and cream.

If I am serving these potatoes with the pilaff I finish off the meal with something light like Crème Caramel. If I omit the potatoes in favour of a green salad then I offer a more substantial sweet such a Bread and Butter Pudding based on a version invented by Anton Mossiman.

CRÈME CARAMEL

600 ml organic whole milk

1½ tbs natural cane caster sugar

2 organic eggs and 2 organic egg yolks

2–3 drops pure vanilla essence

125 gm unrefined natural cane sugar

4 tbs water

Egg whites tend to curdle the mixture so it is important to use more yolks than whole eggs; for a richer custard simply add another yolk.

Add the 125 gm natural cane sugar to the water, bring to the boil and continue boiling until the liquid acquires a light brown colour. Remove from the heat. Add 1 tsp boiling water, stir and pour into a dry warmed soufflé dish. Then carefully turn the mould around until the base and sides are coated with the caramel. Set aside.

Scald the milk. Break the eggs into a bowl, add the extra yolks and beat well with a fork without allowing them to turn frothy. Add the caster sugar, vanilla and milk and stir until the sugar is dissolved.

Strain this mixture into the soufflé mould, cover with foil or a piece of buttered paper and place in the centre of a bain-marie (a roasting dish half-filled with hot water is fine). Bake for 40–50 minutes at (Gas 5 / 190 C). The bain-marie protects the custard from direct heat which can cause curdling. Remove from the heat when it is just set and leave until cooled before turning out.

BREAD & BUTTER PUDDING

250 ml organic whole milk

250 gm organic double cream

2–3 drops pure vanilla essence

Pinch salt

3 large organic free-range eggs

4 bread rolls

40 gm softened organic butter

Scant handful sultanas soaked in hot water

1–2 tbs good quality apricot jam warmed to allow for easy spreading

Bring the cream, milk, salt and vanilla slowly to the boil. Whisk the eggs and sugar and then add the hot liquid, whisking all the time. Pour into another basin through a sieve.

Grease a pie dish with buttered paper. Slice the bread rolls into threes crosswise and butter generously. Arrange them in the pie dish so that the top layer comes above the rim of the dish. Pour in the custard around the sides and leave to stand for an hour. Then cook in a bain-marie for approximately 40 minutes (Gas 3 / 160 C). Remove from the heat, scatter over the drained sultanas and smooth over with the heated jam. Keep heated until ready to serve, with double cream (optional).

If the company is mixed I tend to serve this with custard (made according to directions on the packet) rather than cream as I have yet to meet a man who does not like custard!

During the colder months (November – March) I use a lot of cream-rich recipes, and butter too, because we need the extra warmth despite the fact that central heating is now commonplace. Our bodies, in harmony with Nature are in contractive phase and biologically they are still in tune with our early ancestors. It is a myth that a fat-rich diet makes us put on weight. It is sugar and refined carbohydrates such as white flours, biscuits and junk cereals that add on the pounds. Our bodies are designed to burn fat as fuel and are perfectly equipped to do so. We need approximately 25% of our diet to be fat, mostly unsaturated and from a variety of sources: nuts, oily fish, seeds and legumes which all contain ample quantities of nutritious healthy fat. Once I understood nutrition and gave up dieting in my twenties I have never needed to consciously attempt to lose weight, even after Christmas!

Well, winters may no longer guarantee to come in Dickensian-style but they are still cold enough: heavy rains, bitter frosts and occasional blasts of snow accompanied by freezing winds whipping across from either the Americas or Siberia. No matter what, we are exposed to the rawness of Life on the outside. The days are short, often dark, and the nights long. Time to huddle, gift-wrapped, indoors, and for those of us still fortunate enough, in front of a live fire.

During this time of year I want porridge, a real fire-in-the-belly food if ever there was one. During that period of our history before England was united with Scotland, and skirmishes and forays were regular occurrences up North, the Scots would travel light, carrying a bag of oatmeal and a flat stone alongside their weaponry. They would turn the meal into bannocks by mixing it with water and then cook them on the heated stone. And this would sustain them without so much as a wince in the belly for up to 70 miles on horseback, after which, hopefully they would round up some protein on the hoof to add a little variety to the diet. This was the forerunner of your American cowboy without the tinned beans.

I want contractive foods, that is to say warming foods as opposed to expansive cooling ones because at this time of year our environment is in close-down and conserving energy to sustain itself during its resting phase. Biologically we also close down to some extent only we are probably not aware of this because we have become conditioned mentally to overriding our body signals. The days may be shorter but electricity ensures a constant supply of artificial light and external heat so our lifestyles no longer allow for seasonal distinctions or adjustments.

Instinctively, at this time of year I yearn for plenty of root vegetables, potatoes, and legumes and the meat eaters in the family want roasts. They prefer red meat at this time of the year: sausages and casseroles, alongside the beef and Yorkshire puddings. And speaking of puddings, it is time for steamed sponges, custards, baked apples and dumplings. They want rich broth in preference to soups and consommés – lentils and split peas, barley and pumpkin. And to ensure plentiful supplies of vitamin C, dark green cabbage, broccoli and sprouts.

For vegetarians and vegans, chestnut and nut roasts are particularly sustaining. Nuts and beans are highly contractive (concentrated) foods, full of protein and rich in unsaturated oils; they also contain plenty of minerals such as calcium, magnesium and potassium as well as trace elements such as copper. Sunflower seeds possess zinc, manganese, copper, iron, phosphorus and potassium; and sesame seeds contain good amounts of lecithin, inositol and choline. Black walnuts are 28% protein as opposed to lean beef which is 22% but it is easy to get bogged down in statistics which, taken alone, tend to be useless information.

What we need to remember is that nuts and seeds are designed by Nature to be a highly sustainable winter food. Unshelled they are designed to store for very long periods. Try to obtain nuts from a reputable organic source and enjoy them. They will not make you fat if you eat them as a proportion of your meal rather than a snack!

Nowadays both shelled and unshelled nuts are treated with dyes, preservatives and growth inhibitors (which possibly accounts for the growing number of people demonstrating allergic responses to nuts). Packaged commercial nuts are often fried in saturated fats or hydrogenated oils, which reduce their nutritional value and it may be worth noting, peanuts / groundnuts (the main source of concern as far as allergic reactions go) are not nuts, they are legumes.

Peanut butter is a highly nutritious food. Unfortunately most commercial nut butters are hydrogenated to prevent them going rancid. Rancid fats are suspect because they release free radicals into the system, which can lead to illness. However, the additional hydrogen renders the essential fatty acids in the food nutritionally useless.

It is easy and quick to make your own peanut butter. Pour one cup of shelled nuts either raw or roasted into a grinder. Add one or two teaspoons of organic groundnut oil and a pinch of salt. Grind until smooth or crunchy according to taste.

Several of the recipes in this section contain my favourite nut dishes.

DECEMBER

To sharpen an appetite on a cold day:

A Walking Meditation 6th December 2003 North Northumberland.

It is one of those diamond bright days, piercingly cold with an unyielding frost underfoot. Rather than face exposure on open hills, we drive down into one of the sheltered valleys smothered in a mixture of native trees and planted firs. A stream threads along the valley bottom and is incorporated into a landscaped setting with ponds surrounded by a gravelled path.

Several cars are parked in a semi-circle, their owners scattered into the hills, leaving us alone. We pause, momentarily absorbed by silence overlying the stillness of leafless trees and sombre pines.

To walk in meditation necessitates creating as little disturbance as possible. Simply retain the small individual within the greater whole without intrusion, without any imposition whatsoever. Just being and sensing. Just witnessing. Instead of looking and rearranging and improving, just see.

Upon this tiny fragment of our planet some human hand has fashioned out of the wilderness something accessible and beautiful and named it Wooler Common. Nature and human improvising, each in their own way. Nothing to add, nothing to subtract.

We walk with senses alert through every footfall and its contact with the ground. The foot is a great educator, each step individual, sometimes hesitating, at other times bold, acutely attentive to what is actually there. The feel for the ground comes through the back heel making the initial connection, and spreads upwards and outwards through the arch, across the ball of the foot and along the toes. Even the strongest shoes will not prevent the sensation coming through a foot that is paying attention. And the spring that comes through the back foot rises up, suffusing the whole body, right to the top of the head to bring clarity, to wake us up.

Then the sounds can come through, out of the Silence: the gurgling stream tumbling over the boulders, the chuckle of ducks hidden deep amongst the reeds, the brief chatter of small birds caught up in the shrubbery.

The crunch of the gravel underfoot is sharp, the whisper of sliding grass giving way under the ice, soft.

Against the bright sunlight, vision is sharpened to glimpse a chaffinch at a feeder hanging from a barren twig. A trio of ducks glides seamlessly across a glass pond, and the cold hand of winter rests its palm on the watcher's cheek. The steamy breath rises and falls, and continuing, matches the rhythm of the footfall. Inhalation through the right foot; exhalation through the left. A coming in; a going out. Moving along. In silent witness, feeling what is coming up from the ground; feeling the support; comprehending the strength; the power of gravity through the footfall and the exhalation, followed by the enormous surge of the up-thrust and a lengthening along the spine echoing the inhalation. Then we tune in, we harmonise with the basic rhythm of the planet – expansion, contraction, a coming in, a going out, and in between the pause, the rest, the Silence.

Coming back to the car park, to the point of origin, the circle is complete. Moving out from our still point, our centre, the attention is externalised and the general consensus is to return home. For lunch!

Menu for 8

Sweet and Sour Nut-balls served with Avocado Salad and Leaves.
Aduki Bean Cottage Pie
Baked Pears in Cinnamon and Red Wine

Mix all the ingredients together in a mixing bowl. Shape into walnut sized balls and roll in extra wholewheat breadcrumbs.

Place on a greased baking sheet and bake (Gas 4 / 180 C) for approximately 20 minutes. Remove from the oven, place on a pre-heated plate and keep warm.

For the sauce
Combine 1 tbs arrowroot with ½ a wineglass cider vinegar. Mix in 1 tsp tamari Soya sauce and 1½ tbs runny organic honey. Add 1 tsp vegetable bouillon powder and stir well.

Gently heat this mixture in a heavy-based saucepan, stirring all the time, and as it thickens pour on sufficient vegetable stock to obtain a thick but pourable sauce. Adjust the seasoning.

SWEET & SOUR NUT-BALLS
250 gm mixed milled nuts (no peanuts)

250 gm wholewheat breadcrumbs

1 tbs fresh chopped parsley

½ tsp dried sage

Seasoning

1 free-range organic egg beaten

80 gm grated Gruyere cheese

1 clove garlic crushed

1 finely chopped onion sweated in 25 gm ghee
 or 1 tbs olive oil

I serve this in a large orange-coloured gratin dish containing a mixture of green salad leaves, chopped spring onion and avocado sprinkled with lemon juice and salt.

Scoop the salad to the sides of the dish and place the heated nut-balls in the centre. Pour the sauce over the nut-balls and serve at once on pre-warmed side plates.

Aduki Beans are native to Japan and are considered an important staple food. They have a sweet taste and are easily digestible. For centuries oriental herbalists and bare foot doctors have used these beans to help remedy kidney complaints. To make their prescription soak 2 tbs aduki beans overnight. Drain and rinse. Boil up in approximately 2 litres water until they are soft (about an hour) and at least half the liquid has evaporated. Add a small pinch of sea salt, strain and drink the liquid three times a day.

ADUKI BEAN COTTAGE PIE

125 gm beans soaked overnight

1 clove garlic (optional)

1 onion finely chopped

1 large carrot shredded

1 tbs organic vegetable or tomato puree plus 1 tbs tamari Soya sauce

½ cup white long grain rice cooked in 300 ml salted water

A little oil or ghee to sweat the onion, garlic and carrot

Seasoning + a little grated fresh root ginger (optional)

Sufficient creamed mashed potato to cover a pie dish to a depth of 3 cm

Strain the soaked beans, rinse and place in a saucepan.

Add 600 ml cold water, bring to the boil, cover with a lid and simmer for between 45–60 minutes, adding more hot water as necessary.

Meanwhile soften the garlic, onion and carrot in the oil or ghee. Do not brown. Remove from heat.

Strain the cooked beans retaining the water for stock which can be added to soups, or drunk as a kidney tonic.

Place the beans, vegetables and cooked rice in a large mixing bowl and stir well. Add the soya-sauce, vegetable or tomato puree and mix well. Add sea salt to taste.

Grease a deep pie dish and add the bean mixture, spreading evenly with the back of a spoon or a palette knife.

Mash and cream the potatoes with butter, milk or cream (or a combination) and cover the bean mixture whilst still warm, for ease of spreading. Sometimes I blend into the potato a good tablespoon of creamed horseradish.

Bake the pie in a medium-to-hot oven until the potato is browning on the top. About half an hour (Gas 5–6 / 190–200C)

Serve with Brussels sprouts or dark green cabbage. If using sprouts I allow 5 per person and steam for 10 minutes in a vegetable steamer. Personally I think dark green cabbage tastes better for being boiled for about 20 minutes. I retain the liquid for stock, or to drink with a little tamari added. And just prior to serving I add a knob of butter to either vegetable simply to enrich its flavour.

PEARS IN RED WINE

Allow 1 ripe pear per person. (Ensure the fruit is firm, not soft)

4 tbs natural granulated cane sugar

150 ml water

150 ml red wine

¼ cinnamon stick plus 2 tsp cinnamon

Handful raisins (lexias are particularly good)

A little shredded crystallised citron or orange peel or 1 tsp good quality marmalade

Pinch dried clove or 6 whole cloves

Peel and cut the pears in half, downwards from the stalk, and carefully remove the core. Retain the fruit in a bowl of very lightly salted cold water.

In a large shallow fry pan dissolve the sugar in the wine and water and add the cinnamon stick.

Place the pears in the hot liquid, cored side down and ensure there is sufficient liquid to cover them. If not, I tend to add more wine rather than water, but water is fine. Add the raisins, crystallised fruit or marmalade; sprinkle with powdered cinnamon and poach for about 20 mins until the pears are cooked through but not collapsed! The cinnamon will thicken the sauce; if the liquid has reduced too much add a little hot water at this stage.

Turn off the heat and remove pears with a slotted spoon. Arrange in a warmed shallow serving dish. I use white or blue porcelain to complement the burgundy-coloured sweet. Strain the sauce over the top and keep warm.

Serve with crème fraîche, whipped cream, or yoghurt. Yoghurt is a good counterbalance to the sweetness of the syrup.

If serving this sweet in the summer I omit the citron / orange and the cloves, and reduce the amount of cinnamon by ¼.

In winter the strong pungency of orange and aromatic spices wakens up the senses which become sleepy during the colder months. The pungency sharpens us, keeps us alert and this makes for lively company.

During the summer or early autumn I serve this sweet cold and vary the recipe slightly: I make the syrup in a large saucepan using 200 ml water and 200 ml wine, 6 tbs sugar and a cinnamon stick and boil for one minute. I use whole peeled pears; leave the stalk intact and remove the "eye" at the base. Place the raisins and pears in the syrup, stalk uppermost to prevent discolouration around the cores and poach for 15–20 minutes. Remove the pears and raisins with a slotted spoon and place in a serving dish.

There should be 300 ml liquid. Slake 1 tsp arrowroot with a little cold blackcurrant juice. Add this to the syrup and stir until boiling, reduce the heat and cook until the liquid has cleared. Spoon this thickened syrup over the pears ensuring each pear is well coated. Serve cold with whipped cream or a good vanilla ice cream. There are lots of delicious farm-made ice creams available these days, made without chemicals, or you can make your own.

Note: Cinnamon is good for colds, sore throats and is a natural breath sweetener. It serves as a tonic for the entire digestive system. It can be used as a sedative for mothers during childbirth. It stimulates the glandular system, acts as an antacid, which is useful for stomach upsets.

Note about sugar: (Section Seven)

Spicy Lentil Soup
Brazil nut Bake
Hot Beets and Puréed Roots
Dark Green Cabbage
Tapioca Pudding
Mulled wine

SPICY LENTIL SOUP

2 tbs olive oil or 1 large tbs ghee

2 large onions and 2 fat cloves garlic finely chopped

250 gm split red lentils

600–800 ml cold water

1 bay leaf

½ tsp turmeric

1 tsp finely chopped root ginger

2 tsp curry powder / paste

Sea salt and pepper

Juice of half a large lemon (ensure it is thin-skinned and juicy)

Freshly-chopped parsley and thick cream to garnish

This takes approximately 45 minutes preparation and cooking.

It is a hearty sustaining meal for one of the coldest months of the year. It adorns the table in a riot of colour defiant of frosts, ice, snow-banked gardens and early snowdrops. You come to the table and metaphorically warm your hands at it as you might once have thawed them before a blazing log fire.

I like to serve food in stoneware or earthenware much of the time so my preference is for white table linen as background, and there are so many pretty paper table napkins available to add colour and brightness.

Heat the oil / ghee in a heavy-based pan, add the onion and garlic and cook until transparent. Add the lentils, bay leaf and spices, stirring to incorporate the onions. Add 600 ml water and bring to the boil; turn down the heat, cover and simmer for approximately 30 minutes. Check the consistency: if it is too thick add more water. Season with salt and pepper and then add the lemon juice. At this point you can serve up immediately or, for a smoother consistency, pass through a blender and re-heat. Swirl cream on top and sprinkle with fresh parsley and eat with fresh, organic, wholemeal bread buns.

I have a lovely brown stoneware jug made by Alasdair Hardie, which makes an ideal serving vessel for this soup.

One of my grandmothers had a collection of chocolate brown glazed jugs and something similar to these is still probably available from china outlets.

BRAZIL NUT BAKE

250 gm Brazil nuts chopped small
(but NOT emulsified) in a food processor

1 medium sized onion peeled and finely chopped

1 medium organic green pepper de-seeded and finely chopped

1 clove garlic crushed

2 tbs olive oil

250 gm organic chopped tomatoes
(1 tin will suffice)

2 tsp mixed herbs
(ensure basil and thyme are included)

1 good tsp curry paste

150 gm wholemeal breadcrumbs

1 organic free-range egg beaten (optional)

Sea salt and pepper

A few sprigs of parsley to garnish

The Brazil nut grows on a tree that can ascend to a height of 45m. The nut is reminiscent of a large coconut shell weighing up to 1.8kg and the seeds (what we call nuts) are neatly wedged together. These are a very rich source of protein, fibre, B complex vitamins and minerals: in particular phosphorus, potassium, calcium and iron.

70 gm are estimated to contain 914 calories so, for the calorie conscious, they are better consumed as a main meal than as a snack!

In a heavy-based fry pan soften the garlic, onion and green pepper in the oil. Combine the dry ingredients in a bowl. Add the onion mixture and the tomatoes. Season and mix well. If using an egg, add it at this stage. An egg will bind the mixture, rendering it suitable for slicing when cold, which is how I serve it in summer. It will also enrich it but for egg-sensitive people it is not essential. Spoon the mixture into a greased 500 gm loaf tin, or fluted ovenware flan dish. Bake for 40–45 minutes (Gas 5 / 190 C). If using a loaf tin, invert onto a warmed coloured plate (orange or red will complement it). Decorate with a sprig or two of fresh parsley.

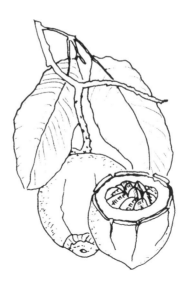

HOT BEETS

For the sauce

50 gm butter

1 heaped tbs cornflour

1 heaped tsp mustard powder

600 ml milk approximately

Sea salt and pepper

Allow one medium or two baby beets per person. Many supermarkets now sell good quality, pre-cooked, organic beets, though I still prefer to cook my own whenever possible. Peeling cooked beets is sensual: under guidance of deft fingertips the dull, leathery skin simply slides off to expose a dark red velvet body.

If using fresh beets, cook in a large pan of unsalted water until the vegetable yields to the point of a very sharp knife. Drain and rinse in plenty of cold water. Peel whilst still warm and arrange in an oven-proof dish. Pre-cooked beets can simply be taken out of their packet and arranged accordingly. Keep warm.

Combine the mustard powder with the cornflour.

Place all the ingredients in a heavy-based pan. Turn on the heat to medium and whisk the mixture continuously with a balloon whisk until it thickens. The texture should be velvety. Pour over the warmed beets and serve immediately or cover with foil and keep warm until required.

If you like a stronger flavour, increase the amount of mustard powder.

PURÉED ROOTS

Use a combination of favourite root vegetables.
For 8 people I would use:

1 medium sized butternut, peeled and de-seeded

2 large carrots scrubbed or peeled

1 large sweet potato peeled

1 large parsnip peeled

Chop the vegetables and steam in a vegetable steamer for 20 minutes or until softened. Turn out into a warmed bowl and mash thoroughly with 10–20 gm butter, salt to taste and a generous measure of freshly ground black pepper.

This is a satisfyingly sweet vegetable combination that harmonises with the hot beets but for those who prefer a sharper contrast try adding a little freshly squeezed lemon juice.

I do not use swede or turnip because I find their individual strong flavour tends to overpower the subtler sweetness of the other vegetables.

DARK GREEN CABBAGE

1 head Savoy cabbage or 1 kg spring greens

Wash thoroughly in plenty of cold water and roughly chop, first removing the centre core, or in the case of Spring greens, the thick portion of the main leaf vein.

In a pan with a well-fitting lid, boil the cabbage briskly in plenty of salted water for 10–15 minutes. Drain, retaining the water for stock, or add a little Vecon and drink. Cabbage water contains masses of minerals and vitamins too precious to give to the waste disposal unit. Place the cabbage in a warmed tureen. Dot generously with butter.

TAPIOCA PUDDING

50 gm tapioca

2 tbs sugar

2 breakfast cups milk

Walnut sized knob butter

A little grated nutmeg (optional)

Tapioca is a bead-like starch obtained from cassava root, one of the staple foods in Africa. It is widely used as a thickening agent, particularly in puddings.

Milk puddings have largely gone out of fashion now but brought to the table occasionally can elicit delighted surprise and exclamations of "Oh, I haven't had that since I was a child!"

Supermarkets no longer seem to offer tapioca, or sago which can be made in exactly the same way. I obtain my supplies from wholefood shops.

Wash the tapioca and place in a buttered pudding dish. Sprinkle over the sugar. Pour on the milk and add the knob of butter. Sprinkle lightly with grated nutmeg and bake in a slow oven (Gas 3 / 170 C) until the pudding is set and browned on top, approximately 1 hour.

MULLED WINE

1 litre, or more, depending on quantity required, full-bodied red wine

½ cup brandy

Juice of 1–2 oranges + 1 or 2 oranges washed and sliced

1 lemon sliced

2 red apples cored and thickly sliced

3–4 tbs organic runny honey

2–3 cinnamon sticks, a small handful of cloves (about 20), ½ tsp grated nutmeg

A dash of orange based liqueur (optional)

Put all the ingredients except the sliced oranges in a large saucepan or preserving pan and heat gently without boiling. Taste for sweetness – if it is too sweet add more orange juice, too sour increase the honey. Strain, pour back into the pan, add the sliced oranges and keep hot until required. Pour into jugs and serve hot.

If ever a month invited a little indulgence with "naughty" foods this is it and, fortuitously, February falls before Lent. This is the month when I am most likely to add herbie dumplings to soups, serve up steamed puddings with toffee sauces, and go wild with the chocolate. We are well into winter and we need a little cosseting to see us through to the end.

On a more practical level, this is a time when I am more inclined to use onions as a vegetable in its own right as opposed to a base for the majority of savoury dishes. The onion family contains antiseptic properties useful as a guard against acute chills and, like garlic, helps to boost the immune system.

It was my grandmother's habit to put a piece of cut raw onion in a shoe and place it beside the bed of anyone laid low with the snuffles. To this day I am not sure whether it was the onion's medicinal attributes or the overpowering stench that persuaded the patient to rally but either way grandma claimed a cure. Folklore warns against leaving a peeled onion exposed for too long prior to use because it will attract germs to itself.

My father's family hailed from Yorkshire and their favourite remedy for a speedy recovery was sitting well wrapped close to a coal fire accompanied by a bowl of hot tripe and onions boiled in milk. An uncle swore by pieces of quartered onion eaten raw, but that is for the desperate, never mind the intrepid.

Menu for 8

Stuffed Onions
Devilled Mushrooms and Rice
Pumpkin and Cashews, Dark Green Buttered Cabbage
Steamed Jam Sponge with Custard

STUFFED ONIONS

8 large onions

4 tbs fresh wholewheat breadcrumbs

1 clove garlic

Handful fresh chopped parsley

1 tsp dried sage

4 small mushrooms

150 gm grated Gruyere
cheese (substitute cashew nuts for vegans)

Salt and pepper

2 tbs lemon juice

200 ml vegetable stock or water
mixed with a little Vecon / vegetable powder.

75 gm crème fraîche (substitute silken tofu for vegans)

Peel the onions and cut off a thin slice from the bottom crosswise; place in a blender.

Carefully remove the rings from the centre leaving only the two outer rings intact. Coarsely chop the onion flesh and add to the blender together with the cheese (or nuts), herbs, mushrooms and half the breadcrumbs. Blend briefly. Stuff the onions. Then arrange them in a gratin dish.

Bring the stock and lemon juice to boiling point; pour a small amount around the onions, sufficient to cover the bottom of the dish, cover with foil and bake in a medium oven (Gas 4 / 180C) for 40 mins or until soft to the point of a knife.

Remove from the oven and discard the foil. Sprinkle the remaining breadcrumbs over the top and place under a high grill to brown for a few seconds. Keep warm.

Add the crème fraîche or tofu to the remaining stock, blend thoroughly and bring to a rapid boil. Pour the sauce around the base of the onions and serve at once with thickly-cut soft white, or granary, bread and olive oil.

DEVILLED MUSHROOMS & RICE

2 cups white basmati rice cooked

1 kg button mushrooms wiped and sliced

Seasoning

1 heaped tsp Dijon mustard

2 tbs plain wholewheat or 85% flour

1 generous tbs ghee or 2 tbs olive oil

2 cloves garlic crushed

1 medium leek finely chopped

Handful chopped, fresh parsley. Save a few sprigs for garnish

500 ml dry cider

A dusting of paprika

To cook the rice
Rinse the rice, place in a large pan and cover with 1.2 litres salted cold water. Bring to the boil and boil rapidly for approximately 5 minutes. Turn off the heat and cover with a tightly-fitting lid for 20 minutes until all or most of the water has been absorbed. Strain if necessary. Turn out into a large, shallow oven proof dish and keep warm.

To make the sauce
Heat the ghee or oil in a large heavy-based frying pan and sweat the crushed garlic and leeks for a few minutes until soft but not browned. Add the mushrooms and parsley; coat well with the fat; cover and turn down the heat; simmer for 5–10 minutes.

Off the heat, stir in the flour and mustard and mix well. Then return to a low heat and slowly add the cider, stirring all the while. The mixture will fizz to begin with. The consistency should be that of thick cream, sufficient to support rather than imprison the mushrooms. If it is too thick add more cider with care.

Return to the rice and using a metal spoon scoop it away from the centre of the dish towards the outer edges. Pour the mushroom sauce into the centre. Garnish with a little fresh parsley and sprinkle with paprika.

PUMPKIN WITH CASHEWS

200 gm salted cashews

1 tbs mustard seed

Sea salt and pepper

1½ tsp ground cumin

1 tsp ground coriander

2 tsp clear honey

1 kg pumpkin or butternut cubed

Roughly chop the cashews and place in the oven warming drawer.

Heat the mustard seed in a little olive oil in a covered heavy-based pan until they pop. Remove the pan from the heat. Add the cubed pumpkin, seasoning and sufficient water to allow the vegetable to cook over a low heat. Add the spices, and honey when the pumpkin is half-cooked through (still quite firm). Cover and simmer until soft but do not allow the mixture to become too dry. Turn out into a pre-warmed dish and fold in the warmed salted cashews, leaving a few to scatter over the top.

Note: Omit the cashews if using the vegan option for the Stuffed Onion starter

DARK GREEN BUTTERED CABBAGE

1 head dark cabbage (Savoy) or spring greens

1 tbs good organic butter

A little lemon juice (optional)

1 tbs cider vinegar

½ tsp sea salt

Thoroughly wash and chop the cabbage, removing the hard centre. If using spring greens take out the main vein from the base of the leaves.

In a heavy pan with a strong lid bring to boil 200 ml water plus 1 tbs cider vinegar. Add the cabbage and cover with the lid. Allow to simmer for 20 minutes checking the water level from time to time. Strain, retaining the liquid for stock or a savoury drink flavoured with tamari, vecon or Worcestershire sauce. Add the butter, lemon juice and sea salt; replace the lid and leave to stand a few minutes on the stove with the heat off to allow the vegetable to absorb the butter. Turn out into a pre-heated tureen and serve immediately.

STEAMED SPONGE & CUSTARD

Weigh two large organic eggs.

Use the same weight of organic butter, natural cane caster sugar, and organic white SR flour.

Using a wooden spoon, cream the sugar and butter in a mixing bowl until white and fluffy.

Whisk the eggs, strain into a small bowl and gradually add these to the creamed mixture, beating thoroughly with a wooden spoon.

Sift the flour twice into a small bowl and fold this into the batter with a metal spoon or spatula.

Lightly grease a 907 gm (2 pint) sized pudding basin and spoon in 1–2 tbs sugar-free jam. Spoon the cake mixture over the top – it should reach no more than two thirds up the sides. Cover with lightly oiled greaseproof paper and foil and place in a steamer filled with rapidly boiling water. Turn down the heat and steam for 1½ hours, checking occasionally to ensure the steamer is not about to boil dry, and add more boiling water from a kettle as necessary.

I have a collection of plastic basins retained from bought Xmas puddings. These come with a lid and make excellent receptacles for steamed puddings. They require no greasing. And the pudding turns out effortlessly. Replace the lid with a pre-warmed inverted plate and turn upside down – the pudding will drop out.

About 10 minutes before the end of the cooking time make the custard according to packet directions. Pour into a large jug and keep warm. Allow one litre for 8 people. More if your guests are male or predominately male!

To turn out from a standard basin, remove the foil and greaseproof paper and simply run a knife around the inside. Place a warmed plate over the top of the basin as above and invert. From here it can be easily transferred to a pre-warmed dish of choice, particularly if you want to serve it in a sea of custard, which I sometimes do for children.

Serve immediately.

SPRING
March – May

INTRODUCTION

Interestingly, up until 1752 when England adopted the new-style Gregorian calendar, New Year fell on March 25th. The Scots, however, designated January 1st as New Year as early as 1600 A.D which might explain why modern New Year celebrations resonated more with the Scots than with Britain as a whole for some considerable time. Only towards the latter part of the 20th century has January 1st been designated a national holiday in England.

The Olde New Year was essentially a celebration of spring, a time of rebirth and renewal, when the sun begins to sport a complexion rather more robust than February's pallor. Late March breathes warmth into the air. Sap stirs in mischievous spirals, tweaking and tugging at sleepy roots, nudging new shoots upward into spearing the ground. Snowdrops and early aconites spread like smiles through the flowerbeds and crocuses and daffodils are not far behind. Suddenly the barren earth is carpeted in colour, a proliferation of white and bright yellows, clear blues and rich purples. Birdsong orchestrates an official end to winter's inertia. March is wake-up time in earnest. Earth is buzzing.

For me it is still too early to start the day with tropical juices. I enjoy a blend of carrot and apple and black grapes with a zing of fresh ginger all through the winter. But from March onwards, a little lemon is good. In fact a slice of fresh lemon in hot water taken first thing will waken up the liver to kick-start the day.

I can dispense with the compulsion for porridge on a daily basis, and maybe have it twice or thrice weekly, with a light muesli on other days. Most beneficial, anytime during the year, is a bowlful of fresh chopped seasonal fruit topped with a little bio-yoghurt, if liked, and a mix of seeds such as sunflower, sesame, flaxseed (linseed), apricot kernels, black onion, and pumpkin.

Pumpkin seeds are an invaluable food for the male's prostate gland, keeping it toned and healthy. I understand the nomads of North Africa chew these daily as they cross the deserts on their camels. Traditionally, at a time when plagues and other pestilence were visited upon humanity, the Prophet Mohammed gave crushed black onion seeds to his followers to ensure their vigour and health. Apart from which, both varieties of seeds are delicious, the latter imparting an aromatic flavour to dishes. They are cheap and easily obtainable from Asian stores.

Stuffed Courgettes with Tomato Salad
Couscous Casserole with Green Salad or Creamed Spinach
Baked Apples and Custard Cream

STUFFED COURGETTES

4 large fat courgettes
halved lengthways to form canoes

50 gm walnuts, hazel nuts or almonds
roughly chopped in a blender

100 gm hard cheese finely grated.

1 onion and one clove garlic
plus 50 gm mushrooms minced

1 medium carrot, 1 large skinned tomato,
1 stick celery, 1 handful fresh coriander,
1 yellow / green pepper

2 tbs cooked wholegrain rice

1 tbs ghee or olive oil

1 tbs organic tomato puree

Sea salt and pepper

A little olive oil for cooking

First prepare the **Tomato Salad**

8 Beefsteak Tomatoes thinly sliced crosswise. Place in a shallow dish and salt generously with sea salt. Set aside.

Carefully hollow out the courgettes and place the flesh in a blender together with the carrot, tomato, celery, pepper and coriander. Mince and set aside.

Sweat the minced onion, garlic and mushrooms in the ghee or olive oil for 2 minutes. Set aside.

In a large mixing bowl combine the rice, walnuts and other raw minced vegetables with the tomato puree. Incorporate the cooked onion mixture and season.

Fill the hollowed out courgettes with the vegetable stuffing and arrange in a large gratin dish. Drizzle a little olive oil around the base of the dish to prevent the courgettes from sticking. Cover with foil and bake in the centre of a medium-hot oven (Gas 6 / 200 C) for 50 minutes. Remove the tinfoil, sprinkle the cheese generously over the top. Then turn up the heat (Gas 8 / 220 C) and cook a further 10 minutes to brown the cheese topping.

Whilst the courgettes are in the final stages of cooking, drain the tomatoes and arrange the slices around the edges of 8 small plates. Drizzle with olive oil (optional).

To serve
Spoon one courgette onto the centre of each individual plate and eat hot.

Variation
Non-vegetarians could substitute the nuts with cooked minced lamb or beef.

COUSCOUS CASSEROLE

250 gm couscous

½ tsp salt dissolved in a cupful of warm water

For the casserole

3 tbs olive oil

1 large onion chopped

2 large carrots scrubbed and diced

250 gm cooked chickpeas

1 tsp each ground cumin, coriander and cinnamon

2 tbs tomato purée

75 gm raisins

450 ml water

1 tbs chopped fresh parsley

2 tsp lemon juice

Sea salt and black pepper

Spread the couscous on a tray and sprinkle with one third of the water. Rub the grains between the fingers and leave for 10 minutes. Repeat this procedure twice more.

In a heavy-based pan gently fry the onion in the oil for approximately 10 minutes. Add the carrots, chickpeas, spices, purée, raisins and water. Bring to the boil and simmer with the lid on for about ½ an hour or until the vegetables are tender.

To cook the couscous

Line a colander or steamer with muslin or a double layer greaseproof paper. Set the steamer over the stew when it is just boiling and cook for about ½ hour. If necessary add more water to the stew.

Then add the lemon juice and parsley to the stew. Adjust the seasoning.

Fork the couscous to ensure the grains are separated and fluffy. Add a little olive oil to enhance the flavour and appearance.

To serve

Place the couscous around a large shallow dish and pour the stew into the centre.

Accompany with a green salad or a tureen-full of steamed spinach into which 1 large tablespoon of crème fraîche has been stirred, and lightly dust with grated nutmeg.

BAKED APPLES WITH CUSTARD CREAM

Allow one large baking apple per person – Bramleys are good.

Wash and core the apples, and arrange in a shallow oven-proof dish.

Three quarters fill the hollowed out centres with raisins or a mixture of raisins, chopped dates, figs and apricots. Add a good teaspoon of Demerara sugar plus a knob of butter.

Cover with foil and bake for an hour or until cooked in a medium oven (Gas 4 / 180 C).

CUSTARD CREAM

600 ml creamy organic milk

4 tbs natural cane caster sugar

2–3 drops of natural vanilla essence

4 organic egg yolks

Pour the milk, vanilla essence and sugar into a pan.

Lightly beat the egg yolks in a bowl; bring the milk to scalding point and pour over the eggs gradually, stirring all the while. Blend well, return to the pan and stir with a wooden spoon over a gentle heat. When the custard coats the spoon and looks creamy strain back into the bowl. Dredge with a little caster sugar to prevent a skin forming

 Caution: Should the custard get too hot and begin curdling pour immediately into the bowl without straining and whisk briskly for a few seconds. Alternatively, pour into an electric blender and blend for a few seconds. It is gentle heat that helps to prevent this happening.

Menu for 8

Leek Vinaigrette with Hot Rolls
Walnut Stuffed Pancakes
Chinese Style Broccoli
Chocolate Pudding or Fresh Figs with Red "Sauce"

LEEK VINAIGRETTE

8 medium leeks

1–2 tbs stoned black olives / garlic stuffed green olives (optional)

1 tbs currants soaked in boiling water for at least one hour, then drained

2 tbs organic tomato/vegetable puree + 1 tbs water

2 tbs cider/balsamic vinegar

4 tbs olive oil

Seasoning

A little Demerara sugar to take away the tartness

Thoroughly wash and trim the leeks. Cut them lengthways from top to bottom and then quarter. Boil for 5 minutes in plenty of salted water; drain; refresh under cold running water and drain again. If necessary place on a clean tea towel and pat dry to absorb excess moisture. Arrange in a shallow dish together with the olives, if using.

Mix the tomato / vegetable puree and water with the oil and vinegar and sweeten to taste. Add the drained soaked currants.

Spoon the dressing over the leeks and set aside for about ½ an hour.

Serve with warm freshly baked granary rolls together with lots of good organic butter or olive oil.

PANCAKES

Quantities allow for one pancake per person.`

Basic pancake mixture for 8 pancakes

125 gm 85% flour

¼ tsp sea salt

1 whole free range egg plus 1 egg yolk

300 ml milk

25 gm melted butter

Sift the flour and salt into a bowl and make a well in the centre. Beat and strain the egg into the well with sufficient milk to mix into a stiff paste with a metal spoon. Gradually add the rest of the milk, beating air into the mixture until the consistency is that of runny cream. Alternatively, place all the ingredients in a blender and whizz round.

Stir in the melted butter and leave for ½ hour. Do not be concerned if the butter forms droplets on the top; these can easily be stirred in as you use the mixture. If using a blender there is no problem, simply whizz the mixture again.

Do NOT substitute oil for butter unless you cannot digest butter. It is the butter which gives the pancakes a lovely crisp texture round the edges, particularly good when serving them as a sweet with lemon and sugar. And butter imparts the best flavour.

Cook the pancakes in a lightly-buttered, eight inch, heavy-bottomed fry pan. Simply pour in sufficient mixture to thinly cover the bottom of the pan. The mixture will begin to bubble. Turn immediately with a metal fish slice, or flip, to cook the underside. Slide the cooked pancake onto a warmed plate and keep each pancake separate with a piece of greaseproof paper. I find once the first pancake has cooked there is no need to re-grease the fry pan as the butter contained in the pancake is sufficient for the task. If there is a tendency for sticking, dot the centre of the pan with a small knob of butter before cooking the next pancake. For the recipe below it doesn't matter too much if the pancake breaks as you can put it together with the filling! And because there is a covering of cheese sauce no one will be any the wiser.

WALNUT STUFFED PANCAKES
makes 8

1 quantity of basic pancake mixture

¾ pint cheese sauce

For the filling

125 gm wholewheat breadcrumbs

200 gm ground walnuts (either process in a food processor or place in a polythene bag and crush with a rolling pin)

1 tsp mixed dried herbs / 1 dsp freshly-chopped oregano, thyme, sage and parsley

1 medium onion finely chopped and lightly fried in a little ghee / olive oil

6 tomatoes skinned and chopped [See below]

Sea salt and freshly ground black pepper

For the cheese sauce

25 gm butter

1 heaped tbs wholewheat plain flour

400 ml approximately whole milk

Sea salt and black pepper

25 gm Gruyere or cheddar cheese grated

Filling

Mix all the ingredients together in a mixing bowl, divide into 8 and place a portion on each pancake. Make an envelope and with the folded side down, pack neatly in a lightly oiled oven-proof dish.

Handy Hint: To skin tomatoes, place in a bowl and cover with boiling water. After a few minutes, remove with a slotted spoon, lightly pierce the skin with the point of a sharp knife and the skin will easily peel off.

Cheese sauce

Melt the butter in a saucepan, stir in the flour to blend and slowly add the milk, bringing to the boil and stirring all the while until it thickens. Stir in the cheese and allow it to melt. Remove from heat and pour over the pancake envelopes.

Place a lid or foil over the top of the dish and bake for 20 – 30 minutes in a moderate oven (Gas 5 / 190 C)

CHINESE STYLE BROCCOLI

2–3 heads broccoli depending on quantity required – taking into account that the stalk will be removed

2 tsp freshly grated root ginger

1 tsp honey and lemon juice

3 tsp tamari and hot water

A little olive oil for stir frying

Thoroughly wash the broccoli, cut off the main stem and separate the heads into small florets.

In a wok or heavy-based deep fry pan, stir fry the broccoli and ginger in olive oil for 5 minutes.

Mix together the other ingredients and pour over the broccoli. Cover the wok and cook for approximately 5 minutes or until just tender.

CHOCOLATE PUDDING

2 heaped tbs cornflour

2 generous tbs good quality cocoa

2 tbs Demerara sugar

600 ml milk approximately

284 ml carton organic double cream.

This is a favourite of mine that takes me back to early childhood. In these health-conscious times it has to be classified as an indulgence but how better to celebrate the end of winter than by indulging a little, and daring to defy an unpredictable cold snap by choosing a cold sweet into the bargain. What is more, it is so simple to make.

In a medium-sized bowl combine the cocoa and cornflour with a metal spoon. Stir in the sugar and blend with a little cold milk to form a smooth paste. This may take a few minutes as the cocoa is reluctant to be managed. Heat the remaining milk and pour slowly onto the paste, stirring all the while with a wooden spoon until thoroughly blended. Rinse out the milk pan, pour in the chocolate mixture and cook over a low heat, stirring vigorously because the mixture will thicken as it comes to the boil. Turn down the heat to its lowest setting and cook for about 5 minutes, stirring continuously whilst ensuring the spoon catches the sides to prevent sticking and burning.

The mixture needs to be the consistency of very thick custard. If it is too thick add a little more milk. You may like to increase the sugar content. I keep the sugar content low because too much sugar will impair the flavour of the cocoa and this is a very rich sweet.

Remove the pan from the heat and pour into a bowl or individual bowls. Sprinkle with a little caster sugar to prevent a skin from forming. Once the pudding has cooled cover with pouring cream and refrigerate. The cream is essential to bring out the strong contrasting flavour of the cocoa.

Note: The main course is biased towards carbohydrate, so you may feel that Chocolate Pudding is tipping the scales too far off balance. It is a matter for common sense: a party of young teenagers will cope very well, whereas those approaching 30 and beyond would probably fare better with the alternative dessert offered. And it may be politically incorrect or sexist, but experience has taught me that men in general will always opt for pudding rather than "dessert" or "sweet". This may not be good for their waistlines but it does wonders for their disposition, and an occasional indulgence never harmed anyone.

FRESH FIGS WITH RED "SAUCE"

Allow 1 or 2 fresh figs per person cut in half north-south.

1 or 2 small rolls soft Welsh goat cheese (optional)

225 gm raspberries (or substitute strawberries / redcurrants)

Vanilla caster sugar to taste – approximately 1–3 tbs [See below]

Preserved stem ginger

1 shallow dish for serving

Fresh figs out of season may be difficult to obtain. You can substitute with dried figs, soaked overnight. Allow 2 figs per person. Carefully pare away the hard stem in the centre and then divide in two and proceed as for fresh figs.

I like to include cheese in this recipe because the colour and textures complement each other; and the sharp slightly sour taste of cheese contrasts well with the deep sweetness of the fig. However, as cheese has been used for the main course you may wish to dispense with it. Use a soft goat cheese roll without a runny centre and slice it, allowing one piece per fig portion. Place this on top of the halved fruits and dot the centre with a sliver of preserved stem ginger.

To make the sauce out of season use raspberries or redcurrants frozen from last summer. Redcurrants will require more sugar than raspberries. Strawberries do not freeze well: thawed they not only utterly collapse but are devoid of flavour and of doubtful nutritional value. Nowadays they can be obtained fresh all year, but strawberries out of season tend to lack flavour and it is difficult to ascertain whether or not they have been irradiated. English strawberries, preferably home grown and eaten in season, are incomparable both for flavour and texture. So fresh strawberries blended in a liquidiser are a superb accompaniment in summertime.

Thoroughly defrost the fruit and place in a shallow bowl. There will be plenty of juice to accompany the pulp. Scatter sparingly with sugar. Allow to rest for 30 minutes. Rub the fruit through a nylon strainer and check the sweetness, adding more sugar if required. Pour the puree into the shallow serving dish and arrange the figs (with or without cheese and ginger) on top.

If you prefer a thicker sauce use a little arrowroot slaked in 1 tbs cold water. Add this to the purée and cook over a low flame until the sauce thickens. Allow to cool and then pour into the serving dish.

Note: Vanilla Sugar is very simple to prepare. Simply pour the caster sugar into an airtight jar. Stick a vanilla pod down through the centre. Cap and leave. The sugar will be flavoured after a month. You can keep refilling the jar with sugar.

Fresh Juice
Mushroom Goulash with Beetroots in Sour Cream
or Leek Bake
Mixed Salads
Compôte of Dried Fruits

FRESH JUICE
Suggestion for 8 people

4 medium–large organic carrots

2 sweet eating apples

2 black plums

½ pineapple

2 pears

A walnut sized piece fresh root ginger

Using a juicer, blend a variety of fruits and / or vegetables. Strain into a glass jug or separate glasses and garnish with a sprig of fresh mint.

If this yields insufficient juice top up with fresh organic orange or apple juice.

For a simpler drink use one type of fruit with carrot and ginger.

Apple and carrot marry well.

Apple and cranberry is another good combination and is a tonic for the bladder. It is fairly astringent and tangy

Raspberry and orange is delicious during the summer months. In fact all the tropical fruits such as pineapple, mango and papaya taste much nicer than the carton juices when freshly pressed. The enzyme and vitamin content is higher too.

If you do not possess a juicer, use a liquidiser and strain.

One of my favourite summer drinks requires a liquidiser rather than a juicer. **Lemon Honey Drink** is an example of necessity being the mother of invention.

During the 1970s I lived on the sunny East Coast of New Zealand's North Island. Every garden must have boasted at least one lemon, grapefruit and orange tree. We had an avenue of 30 lemon trees which, one year, had not been fully stripped of fruit before the next crop was ripening.

The trees were so over-laden with fruit the branches were in danger of snapping, and such was the abundance of produce throughout Poverty Bay it was impossible to give them away at the gate. Fortunately there was the local lemonade factory even though the glut of citrus meant they could offer only 10 cents per kilo.

To my amazement I collected $70.00 so you can imagine the number of car boot loads I drove down to the factory. Notwithstanding the sale, we had sufficient lemons to drink them fresh every day during the soaring temperatures of a long, long summer.

Lemons apart, we were friendly with a local honey supplier whose bees produced excellent honey.

LEMON HONEY DRINK

2 large, juicy, organic lemons – if you cannot obtain organic at least use unwaxed lemons and scrub well

1/3 –1/2 jar runny organic honey

Cold, boiled water

Wipe the lemons and cut into 8 pieces. Place in a liquidiser with the honey and fill with water. Whizz for a minute or two and strain into a large jug. Drink immediately or chill for 1/2 an hour. Add a little fresh chopped mint for garnish if liked.

If kept for 24 hours the juice takes on a bitter taste reminiscent of manufactured Bitter Lemon (without the additives)

All my family loved this drink and so did the children's friends and I am convinced it enhanced their natural fresh complexions. It most certainly ensured an abundant intake of vitamin C.

MUSHROOM GOULASH

50 gm ghee or 2 tbs olive oil

1 large onion finely chopped

375 gm mushrooms wiped and sliced

2 red peppers de-seeded and finely chopped

3 tsp paprika

4 tbs vegetable stock

300 ml plain yoghurt

20 gm wholewheat plain flour

2–3 hard-boiled organic free-range eggs

A little chopped fresh parsley

Melt the butter and cook the onions and peppers for a few minutes before adding the sliced mushrooms. Season, add stock. Cover and simmer 15 minutes.

Blend the flour, yoghurt and 2 tsp paprika. Stir into the mushroom mixture and heat through gently, adding a little more stock or water, if necessary, as it cooks and thickens. Cook for 5 minutes, stirring. Pour into a pre-heated ovenproof dish and sprinkle with chopped hard-boiled eggs, 1 tsp paprika and fresh parsley.

Serve with:-

Plain Boiled Basmati Rice.

Allow 1/4 cup dry rice plus 100 ml fresh salted water per person.

Wash the rice, add it to the water and steam in an electric steamer for 20 minutes.

Alternatively bring the rice and water –150 ml salted water per 1/4 cup of rice – to a slow boil on the top of the stove. Stir to ensure the rice is not sticking and allow a brisk boiling for no more than five minutes. Cover the pan and turn off the heat. Allow 15 minutes for the rice to absorb the water and turn out into a pre-warmed dish. If the rice has not absorbed all the water, strain before spooning into the pre-heated dish. Stir in a walnut sized knob of butter prior to serving.

BEETS IN SOUR CREAM

Allow one or two small cooked beets per person and quarter them.

Place in a deep dish and cover. Warm through in a moderate oven. Pour sufficient soured cream over the top to cover the beets and keep warm. Just prior to serving lightly stir the beets to ensure they are coated but take care not to render the cream entirely pink as this will spoil the effect of the colour contrast. If sour cream is unobtainable, whip up some whipping or double cream and stir in the juice of half a lemon. Taste. If you prefer a sharper taste add a little more lemon. The sharp flavour contrasts well with the sweetness of the beets.

I like to serve this vegetable with the goulash because the colours combine so well, and a **Mixed Salad** of lambs leaves, rocket and baby spinach balances the entire meal.

LEEK BAKE

Half fill a deep pie dish with peeled, thinly-sliced, floury potatoes; season with sea salt and pepper and cover the bottom of the dish with a little cold water to prevent the potatoes from drying out. Add scrubbed chopped leeks to almost fill the dish. Cover with tinfoil or a well-fitting lid and bake in a moderate to hot oven for 40–60 minutes (Gas 6–7 / 200–210 C.)

Remove from the oven and check that the potatoes yield to the point of a sharp knife. Spread 150 gm soft Welsh goats' cheese over the leeks; add 150 ml carton double cream, and then sprinkle with a generous handful shaved Gruyere cheese. Replace the lid / tinfoil, return to the oven and bake for a further 30–40 minute. If you prefer a browned topping remove the cover after 10 minutes.

Serve with a generous bowlful of green salad leaves, thinly-sliced cucumber and garlic-stuffed olives.

This bake also makes a suitable supper dish served with warm baby beets minus the sour cream.

COMPÔTE OF DRIED FRUITS

450 gm mixed dried fruit from Health Shops

½ bottle red wine

1 tbs clear organic honey

1 cinnamon stick

A few pieces stem ginger thinly sliced.

1 large carton thick bio yoghurt

Soak the fruit overnight. Remove the fruit with a slotted spoon and place in an earthenware casserole. In a separate pan bring the wine, honey, and spices to the boil. Pour over the fruit, cover the dish with a lid and cook for 1 hour in a pre-heated, slow oven (Gas 2 / 150 C). Serve warm with thick yoghurt.

Summer witnesses Nature at Her peak of creativity, a drawing together of energies in a final flamboyance of colour reminiscent of Spanish flamenco. The perfumed air is vibrant with insect dervishes, strident bees and flitting butterflies. Yet behind this frenetic burst of activity lies a faint echo of indolence, a hint of quieter times heading over the horizon. Evenings lengthen, tapering noon day brightness into softer hues of lilac and rose. Buzzing subsides to a hum down the throat of foxglove, butterflies linger on the evening primrose and intoxicating scents of rose drift across lawns towards smoking barbecues.

Amidst the tinkle of wine glasses and easy laughter we are oblivious to time passing. Summer is essentially for being, celebrating company, and congeniality. In this, more than any other season, we are aware of the lightness in which we are immersed: in our surrounds, our demeanour, our dress, our very essence. Summer means holidays, rest from endeavour. At no other time is it so easy to harmonise with all-that-is-not-us, to bring us back to our senses, to become acutely attentive to Beauty. Summer is the Young in all of us. It lies at the edge of Eden. We can breathe outdoors into infinity. We open. We flower. We fulfil dreams and realise possibilities. Summer is the springboard to the promise of our future. Summer is the deep abiding present presence.

Rainfall in summer is gentle. Unlike winter squalls, and sharp penetrating springtime showers, there is warmth and depth to summer rain. It penetrates because the earth yields to it. After summer rain the earth feels soft, quenched, and gratitude is expressed in a bouquet of perfume emanating from the flowerbeds, particularly where the borders are herbaceous.

Herbs are for the most part humble plants. Many are known as common, many thrive on soils too poor to sustain the more exotic cultivations. They are tenacious; they house wisdom older than humankind. They are judicious and potent. They can be subtle, they are always honest. Possessed of a power to cure and kill, herbs are our medicine and our poison. They seek nothing other than respect.

In past times most gardens would allow space for herbs. The still room was an important adjunct to the mediaeval kitchen and probably featured in many households well into the early 20th century. The aristocracy apart, it was part of a woman's education to be as versed in herbal lore as in cooking and needlework since the household's wellbeing depended on her knowledge of physicke. *"The Diary of a Farmer's Wife 1796 –1797"* published by Penguin, gives a marvellous insight into how Anne Hughes took responsibility for the welfare of her extended family. She includes recipes for buttercup concoctions and pansie wine, the one being medicinal, the other recreational.

Flowers were in common usage as food as well as adornment. A favourite of mine, which can be incorporated into a salad, is nasturtiums stuffed with cream cheese.

Borage flowers floated on a bowl of homemade lemonade, iced tea or punch add a touch of delicacy and charm to the table, and violets are still used in confectionery as violet creams or sugared violets.

Many folk remedies, often derided as "old wives' tales", will have derived from common knowledge distilled down the ages from woman to woman. My great grandmother, Sarah, used her scullery as a still room, and my maternal grandmother's first recourse was to the herbalist in preference to the doctor even after medical care became free under a nationalised Health Service.

Prior to the development of the vacuum cleaner, housewives and housemaids spent hours scrubbing and cleaning on their knees, hence the term "housemaid's knee". A well-known remedy for rheumatism or swollen knees invoked the humble cabbage leaf. Take one or more outer leaves from a large green cabbage. Remove the central vein and scald the leaf until softened. Cool a little so as not to burn the flesh and wrap as hot as can be withstood around the joint, and bandage. The inflammation will be drawn out.

One of my aunts derived some relief from this remedy but since her knee problems derived more from overweight than physical overwork it is probably no surprise a cure was not effected. At least she was spared possible side-effects from a prescribed anti-inflammatory.

Today most herbs are bought prepared and dried, though the commoner ones such as parsley, coriander and basil can often be obtained relatively fresh from supermarket outlets. For the most part they are used sparingly. Herbal potency is well demonstrated by thyme whose tiny leaf is disproportionate to the pungency released when pressed between finger and thumb; and the taste is equally strong. There are several varieties of thyme well worth cultivating both for appearance and flavour. Lemon thyme goes particularly well with lamb as an alternative to rosemary, and it is good in rice dishes too.

The subject of cultivation and usage of these wonderful plants is too vast to incorporate here. Two of my favourite treatises are Juliette de Baïracli Levy's *"Illustrated Herbal Handbook"*, published by Faber and Claire Lowënfeld and Philippa Back's *"The Complete Book of Herbs and Spices"* published by David and Charles.

Maybe common interest in the subject has not waned so much as changed direction. Public awareness and interest in aromatherapy as part of a burgeoning interest in complementary therapies has resulted in a proliferation of printed material readily available.

But of necessity, the use of herbs in this book will adhere to the kitchen rather than the bathroom!

Marinated Beans
Mushroom Croustade
Chocolate and Orange Mousse or
Coffee Ice cream

MARINATED BEANS

For the marinade combine

6 tbs olive oil

2 tbs cider vinegar

1 tsp clear honey

1 tbs chopped fresh thyme

Sea salt and black pepper

This keeps well in a screw-top jar.

Steam 500 gm top-and-tailed green beans for approximately 10 minutes. They need to retain their firmness to the touch of a sharp knife-point. Pour the marinade over the hot beans and toss well to ensure they are coated thoroughly. Allow to stand for a few hours.

Broad beans are equally good combined with 2 chopped and cored red eating apples. I add the apple just prior to serving.

Serve with thick chunks of French bread and olive oil or butter and a salad of mixed leaves (include some raddichio) or sliced and salted beefsteak tomatoes cut crosswise and sprinkled with black pepper.

MUSHROOM CROUSTADE

For the croustade

200 gm soft wholemeal breadcrumbs /
150 gm soft white breadcrumbs

150 gm ground almonds

50 gm butter (vegans use butter substitute)

125 gm flaked almonds finely chopped

1 clove garlic

½ tsp mixed dried herbs

For the topping

500 gm washed and sliced organic closed cup / chestnut mushrooms

50 gm butter (or butter substitute)

2 heaped tbs plain organic flour

450 ml milk / Soya milk

Sea salt, black pepper, nutmeg

4 large tomatoes skinned and sliced [See April]

1 tbs fresh chopped parsley.

First make the croustade by combining the breadcrumbs and ground almonds. Rub in the butter as for making pastry and stir in the flaked almonds. Crush the garlic and add to the mixture alongside the dried herbs. Mix well and press firmly into the base of an oven-proof dish or Swiss roll tin. Bake in a hot oven (Gas 8 / 225 C) for 15 minutes until crisp and golden. Remove from the oven and set aside.

Meanwhile make the topping: sauté the mushrooms in the butter until tender, add the flour and when it froths remove from the heat to stir in the milk. Return to the heat and stir until thickened; simmer over a very low heat for a few minutes and season well with sea salt, pepper and grated nutmeg.

Spoon the mushroom mixture over the croustade, top with the skinned tomatoes and sprinkle very lightly with salt and pepper. Return to a moderately heated oven (Gas 4 / 180 C) to heat through and serve sprinkled with fresh parsley.

Suggested accompaniments
Creamed or roasted potatoes, depending on the weather – if it is cool I go with roasted potatoes, if warm then creamy mashed potatoes are very good.

Lightly steamed broccoli, celery, and carrots cut into matchsticks.

CHOCOLATE & ORANGE MOUSSE

250 gm good quality dark chocolate (at least 70% cocoa solids)

2 tbs fresh orange juice

Grated rind one organic orange

1 tbs orange curaçao / brandy

4 large free range eggs separated

Whipped cream for garnish (optional)

Toasted flaked almonds (optional)

Melt the chocolate over a pan of boiling water. Remove from heat. Stir in the juice and orange rind, then the liqueur and, finally, the egg yolks. Whip the whites into stiff peaks and gently fold into the cooled chocolate mixture with a metal spoon using a cutting and folding movement. Refrigerate for at least 2 hours and serve as it is or garnished with whipped cream and toasted, flaked almonds.

This is a very rich dessert and a little goes a long way!

COFFEE ICE CREAM

(1 cup = standard-sized teacup)

1 ½ cups double cream

½ cup jersey / creamy full-fat milk

2 large organic eggs

¾ cup natural cane sugar

2 tbs very strong black coffee (espresso)

1 tbs brandy / curaçao / cointreau

This treasured recipe comes courtesy of my good friend and yoga student, Jenny. It requires no excuse for indulgence but is particularly comforting after a long yoga workshop!

Beat the eggs, milk and cream together and then slowly add the sugar, beating continuously. Blend in the coffee and liqueur. Freeze in trays for about 2 hours. Remove from freezer and allow to thaw a little. Beat again to obliterate any ice crystals and refreeze in a container with a lid. Remove from freezer and store in refrigerator for ½ an hour prior to serving.

These amounts will yield approximately ¾ litre delicious ice cream. The addition of a little liqueur ensures the consistency is soft rather than rock-hard.

Curried Eggs on a bed of Watercress
Pasta Cheese Bake with Avocado and Mixed Leaf Salad
Cardamom Fruit Salad or Strawberry Flan

CURRIED EGGS

Allow 1 hard-boiled egg per person

50 gm butter

1 tsp organic garlic mayonnaise (or any good mayonnaise combined with 1 small clove crushed garlic) and an equal quantity thick natural or Greek yoghurt, a dash of lemon juice and a generous pinch dry mustard powder

Sea salt and pepper

1 tsp curry powder (mild/medium/hot according to preference)

¼ tsp paprika (optional)

1–2 tbs basic salad dressing [See below]

2 bunches watercress

Divide the eggs lengthways, remove the yolks and mash thoroughly with the curry powder. Soften the butter and work into the yolks with the mayonnaise mixture. Cover. Keep the whites fresh in a bowl of iced water.

Clean and coarsely chop watercress; drizzle the basic salad dressing lightly over the top and spoon round the edge of a flat serving dish.

Remove the egg whites from the water, drain on a clean cloth and pat dry. Fill with the creamed yolk mixture, reshape the eggs and arrange them on the narrow bed of watercress.

Scatter some salad leaves in the centre of the dish. Serve with chunks of fresh, warmed granary bread.

BASIC SALAD DRESSING
In a blender

⅓ cup organic cider vinegar

1 cup virgin olive oil

1 heaped tsp medium or hot curry powder

Sea salt and pepper

1 large clove garlic crushed

1 dsp good quality honey

1 scant tsp mustard powder

1 tsp dried mixed herbs or 1 tbs finely chopped fresh parsley, marjoram and thyme

This is easy to prepare, stores well, and can be used in a variety of recipes.

Blend. It will emulsify and can be stored in an airtight jar. Over time the dressing will separate out but simply shake the jar well before using. If using fresh herbs I store the dressing in a refrigerator and use within 3 weeks.

PASTA CHEESE BAKE

Allow 2-3 cannelloni shells per adult

For the sauce

150 ml olive oil

1 large chopped onion

1–4 cloves garlic crushed

2 cans organic chopped tomatoes plus an equal amount water

1 tube organic tomato / vegetable puree

2 sprigs parsley

1 tsp mixed dried herbs – basil, thyme and oregano

1 tsp Demerara sugar

Sea salt and pepper

For the filling

1 kg ricotta or curd cheese

250 gm finely diced mozzarella

$1/3$ cup grated parmesan

2 large free-range eggs

1 tbs fresh finely chopped parsley

Sea salt + 2 tbs grated parmesan

Make the sauce first

Sweat the garlic and onion in the oil, then add all the other ingredients, bring to the boil and simmer on a low heat for 15 minutes. Keep warm.

In a large bowl mix the ricotta and mozzarella cheeses, add the parmesan and stir in the parsley. Beat the eggs; stir thoroughly into the cheese mixture. Season.

Stuff this mixture with the end of a small spoon into the cannelloni shells. This takes time so be patient!

Grease a large oven-proof gratin dish and line the base with the stuffed shells. Cover with the tomato sauce. Place a lid on top and bake for 30–40 minutes in a preheated oven (Gas 5 / 190 C).

Sprinkle with parmesan prior to serving.

Accompany with a large bowl of mixed salad leaves and chopped avocado dredged in olive oil and lemon juice.

CARDAMOM FRUIT SALAD

Make a syrup by simmering for 5 minutes:

Cardamom soothes the stomach and is ideal as an accompaniment to a heavy meal. It is also an appetite stimulant, is often used to flavour unpleasant medicines and is an ingredient of eau-de-cologne!

150 ml each of water, clear honey

The juice of ½ lemon

¼ tsp ground cardamom.

When cool strain over a basic fruit salad comprising:

Allow the syrup to permeate ½ an hour prior to serving and accompany with a bowl of Greek yoghurt, fromage fraîs or whipped cream.

1 grapefruit

1 orange

2 bananas

2 sliced red eating apples

The juice of ½ lemon and a light sprinkling of ground cardamom

For a more exotic salad add mango, papaya and kiwi fruit.

STRAWBERRY FLAN

3 large free-range eggs

75 gm caster sugar

50 gm plain flour

40 gm organic butter melted

25 gm ground almonds

Strawberries (allow sufficient to generously cover a 23 cm flan)

Grease a 23 cm round cake tin and line the base with non-stick greaseproof paper.

Wash, rinse and pat dry the strawberries. Leave the largest strawberry whole; slice the rest in half. Arrange on a large plate and dust with a little caster sugar (optional). Set aside.

Whisk the eggs and sugar at high speed in a blender until thick and creamy.

Gently fold in the flour and almonds with a metal spoon and then carefully stir in the melted butter. Pour into the prepared cake tin and bake in a pre-heated oven (Gas 4 / 180 C) for approximately 30–35 minutes until risen and beginning to shrink from the sides of the tin.

Turn out and leave to cool.

Just prior to serving, place the whole strawberry in the centre and organise the halved fruit over the flan to cover. Serve with lashings of whipped cream flavoured with a drop or two pure almond essence and a little caster sugar to sweeten.

Avocado Soup
Rice Salad with Fresh Tuna or Tofu Burgers
Gooseberry Fool

AVOCADO SOUP

3 large ripe avocados

1½ tbs lemon juice

2 ½ pints ice cold milk

Sea salt and pepper

2 generous tbs chopped chives

2 medium–large sticks celery

Peel and stone the avocados. Place everything except the chives in a liquidiser and blend. Chill. Add the chives prior to serving.

Serve with Melba toast.

To make Melba toast
Toast some thick slices of white bread. Cut off the crusts and using a sharp knife cut through each slice of toast crosswise. Toast the exposed undersides and leave to cool. The toast will be crisp when cold.

RICE SALAD

250 gm basmati rice

2 tbs organic raisins

1 green and 1 red pepper de-seeded and finely diced

¼ cucumber finely chopped

1 bunch spring onions trimmed and chopped

50 gm pinenuts

½ small packet frozen peas cooked

1 sweet corn cooked and de-husked

1 stick celery scrubbed and chopped

1 Granny Smith apple cored and chopped

A good handful fresh chopped parsley

Basic Salad Dressing (This Section – July)

Cook the rice. Rinse and drain under cold running water. Place in a large mixing bowl and combine with all the other ingredients. Stir in, a little at a time, sufficient basic salad dressing to thoroughly coat the rice grains, but without leaving a trail of dressing in the bottom of the bowl.

Turn into a glass serving bowl and serve with grilled fresh tuna steaks or tofu-burgers.

TUNA STEAKS

Allow one steak per person.

Cover the grill pan with a piece of foil and arrange the tuna on top.

Brush with a little oil or melted butter. Lightly season with sea salt and pepper and grill on both sides. Check with a knife point that the steaks are cooked through and serve on pre-heated plates.

Alternatively, you can pan-fry the steaks in a mixture of ghee and olive oil.

TOFU BURGERS

375 gm tofu

75 gm organic rolled oats

1 large organic carrot grated

1 finely grated onion

1 tsp fresh root ginger grated

1 tsp mixed dried herbs (include basil and oregano)

1½ tsp tamari sauce

Sea salt and pepper

25 gm oatgerm or wheatgerm for coating

Heat the oven (Gas 5 / 190 C).

Drain the tofu, retaining the liquid for stock.

Mash the tofu and mix in all the other ingredients. Allow to stand 1 hour. Shape into 8 burgers and dip in the oats / wheatgerm.

Bake on a greased tray for 15–20 minutes.

Nutritional Note: Tofu has one of the lowest ratios of fat to protein of any plant food. 25 gm contains just over 20 calories.

2 burgers will provide about 8 gm protein which equates with 50 gm all-beef-no-added-cereal burger.

GOOSEBERRY FOOL

250 gm fresh gooseberries plus extra for decoration

3 tbs caster sugar

175 ml double cream

175 ml thick yoghurt

Put the gooseberries and sugar in a food processor and blend. Add the cream and yoghurt and process until the cream forms soft peaks. Serve in individual glass dishes and decorate with a single gooseberry and a few leaves.

Rhubarb can be substituted for gooseberries: clean and chop the rhubarb and cook in a heavy-based saucepan until soft, with sugar to sweeten. If you grow Sweet Cicely you can cook some leaves with the fruit and reduce the sugar content. Angelica stem will also impart a lovely flavour.

Nutritional Note: Sweet Cicely is of value to those wishing to reduce their intake of sugar and to diabetics. It grows profusely between February and November, ensuring a plentiful supply of leaves for most of the year, but do remember to remove the flower heads as they blossom, otherwise little goodness will be retained in the leaves and it will quickly go to seed.

BREAKFAST

Quaintly, convention yet maintains breakfast should be the biggest meal of the day, followed by a hearty lunch and, in the evening, a light dinner or supper. The traditional English breakfast, called the Full English Breakfast by catering establishments, comprises bacon, egg, sausage, tomato, mushrooms, baked beans and sometimes black pudding – all to follow fruit juice, fruit and cereal, and accompanied by a rack of toast and bread rolls.

In the 18th century a gentleman's breakfast was a veritable banquet, offering eggs, cooked viands and cold cuts as well as a variety of fish dishes. To confront such an enormity of food, let alone digest it, required time and leisure to an extent that would be impractical in this day and age, and utterly impossible for the average commuter struggling with time management from the first shrill of the alarm clock.

Many people cannot face even the idea of breakfast first thing in the morning and would prefer to arrive at work on a swallow of coffee or tea and then think about eating after an hour at the computer. The mid-morning snack is really breakfast in this situation.

One argument in the pro-breakfast lobby's favour is that blood-sugar levels tend to be low first thing in the morning. Low blood sugar can cause feelings of tiredness, lethargy and an inability to cope. Eating a good breakfast will not only help stabilise blood-sugar levels, it will lessen cravings for snacking or over-eating later in the day and thus reduce the likelihood of gaining unwanted weight.

It could be argued that we do not need the breakfasts of our antecedents, because our lives are, for the most part, less physically challenging. Even the traditionally manual industries from farming to mining now boast technological aid; and most of us enjoy the benefits of central heating, if not at home, then in a working environment. So we do not require food as fuel to the degree our forebears did.

However, we still require food for nourishment and repair and we do have to break the night fast at some stage of the day. It makes sense to take our main meal during the day, when we have the opportunity to expend the energy produced, rather than at night when the digestive system has slowed down and is not at all happy to begin a biological night-shift.

Unfortunately in the sacred name of Efficiency, the lunch hour seems to have shrunk to the lunch ½ hour when rationally it would merit being expanded to 1½ hours. This would allow time to digest a good-sized meal, when energies are peaking around noon, and for rest afterwards prior to working through the afternoon. We would probably arrive home less exhausted and Production, that gospel of our linear pundits, would doubtless increase rather than reduce – simply because we would operate more efficiently alongside our machines. There would be less wastage from an inability to maintain attention.

Studies have shown that children fed a wholesome diet rather than a junk one comprising fizzy drinks, sweets and crisps have longer attention spans, are engaged and less disruptive. In other words their behaviour improves in all senses and successful outcomes can only enhance personal self-esteem, another buzz-word of our times.

During the eighties and nineties, when I lived on Tyneside, it was commonplace for children to stream into the local newsagent / sweetshop on their way to school and buy a breakfast of flavoured crisps, toffee crumble, choc lik and artificially flavoured water. These were not socially deprived children; they came from so-called "good" homes. I noticed they yawned a lot, looked exhausted, presented poor posture and literally dragged their feet along the pavement as far as the car waiting to transport them to the school gates. Time could be a problem: breakfast is traded for an extra half-hour in bed! And maybe there is no appetite for breakfast if the system is still clogged with the midnight munchies. I am not scapegoating Tyneside; if anything current concerns about national obesity levels suggest the region is the rule rather than the exception.

How and when we choose to eat is a matter of lifestyle. We benefit from being informed in order to make rational choices and take personal responsibility for our lives. Skipping breakfast may not be inadvisable in itself, but when we do eat, biology requests that we consider eating real food as opposed to a laboratory designed substitute.

The following recipes are offered as augmentation for those who do indulge in breakfast and as tantalisation for those who might be tempted to try it. Anyone for whom breakfast is anathema ..... just skip it!

Think Porridge!

Porridge is definitely a matter of individual taste. One person may like it made with whole milk, liberally sweetened and enhanced with cream, another will prefer it made with water and eaten with salt. It is a dish traditionally associated with the Scots and when visiting Scotland the English invariably request it for breakfast even in the height of summer. Somehow it seems to taste better made in Scotland by the Scots! Could there be something in the water? On Summer Yoga Retreats in Scotland I have found demand for the porridge to be insatiable, so it is just as well we allow two hours between breakfast and practice or "becoming grounded" could be down to more than the force of gravity.

Porridge, in our culture, is synonymous with oats but other cereals lend themselves equally as a porridge base in consistency, flavour, and nourishment. Every cereal is endowed with unique properties. Oats, for instance, possess a gummy fibre to which excess cholesterol can attach itself and thence be safely eliminated from the body. It is a grain associated with the warmth element so is particularly suitable as a winter food.

SIMPLE PORRIDGE
Method 1

Make according to packet directions or 1 part cereal to 10 parts milk, water or a combination. It is difficult to give exact measurements as the best consistency is determined by personal preference. The rolled oat variety is cooked up in about five minutes from boiling point, oatmeal takes about 20 minutes. Gradually add the liquid to the cereal in a heavy-based pan and bring to the boil stirring consistently. A pinch of salt will bring out the flavour of the oats.

SIMPLE PORRIDGE
Method 2

Allow 1 heaped tbs organic rolled oats per person

½ tsp sea-salt

Water / milk or a combination of the two. Alternatively use Soya milk

Place the oats in a heavy-based saucepan, add the salt and sufficient liquid to form a creamy sauce. Leave overnight to soak.

In the morning add enough liquid to obtain a runny consistency and slowly bring to the boil, stirring as it thickens, and adding more liquid if necessary until the required consistency is obtained.

Serve hot.

The flavour can be enhanced with any one or a combination of the following: raisins, Demerara sugar, honey, or syrups made from maple, rice or barley, hot / cold milk, Soya milk or cream, salt.

Any leftovers can be re-heated the next day. Some people like to eat it cold when it has set.

Other varieties of oats can be cooked just as easily: fine and pinhead oatmeal or jumbo rolled oats are ideally soaked overnight. If you have an Aga the porridge can be cooked slowly overnight.

MILLET FLAKES

These produce an excellent flavour and contain more iron than any other cereal. It was possibly the first cereal grain to be cultivated for domestic purposes and was the staple food in China long before rice was introduced there about 12,000 years ago. It is a highly respected food in India, parts of Africa and Asia, particularly amongst the Hunza people where it forms an essential part of the diet. Hunzas are famed for their robust health and longevity. It makes a wonderful food for infants and young children, not to mention teenagers, particularly for girls at the onset of puberty, if they can be persuaded!

GROUND RICE

This cereal makes a very smooth porridge although we might be excused for thinking of it as a sweet dessert rather than porridge. It combines very well with raisins, prunes, or other soaked dried fruit such as figs or apricots. Ground rice is an excellent food for infants and so is flaked barley.

BREAKFAST ANYTIME

FRESHLY SQUEEZED
FRUIT or VEGETABLE JUICES

Examples: grapefruit, orange or bottled organic juices.

If you possess a juice extractor the following combinations lend an interesting start to the day:

2 carrots + thumb-sized piece root ginger. Top up with organic orange juice.

Apple, pear, carrot

Apple and ginger

Nectarine, plum, peach and ginger

Carrot, beetroot, ginger and apple

The combinations are endless and, once you start, you will quickly find you develop your own according to your individual preferences. All these suggestions can be augmented with carton juices. I tend to stick with the organic varieties such as orange, apple and cranberry.

A small glass per person is sufficient.

As mentioned earlier, a glass of hot water with a slice or squeeze of fresh lemon will kick-start the liver to help boost your energy levels.

FRESH FRUIT, SEEDS & YOGHURT

Chop or slice a variety of fresh seasonal fruit. In the summer the choice will be greater than in the winter, where you will be restricted to apples, plums and pears. Dried fruits such as figs, prunes, apricots soaked overnight will add interest to a winter breakfast.

If the fruit is for a family rather than an individual it can be prepared as for a fruit salad, put into a large bowl and then served out individually. The fruit can be eaten alone or combined with seeds and / or yoghurt.

Nuts and seeds contain a wealth of essential minerals, vitamins and fatty acids. The roughage is excellent for elimination. If using linseeds ensure you drink a generous amount of water throughout the day for maximum benefit.

Sprinkle on some chopped or flaked almonds, and a selection of seeds such as sunflower, pumpkin, sesame, black onion and linseeds. I use processed linseeds such as Linusit Gold or Bio-Linseeds because I find them easier to digest. I also use apricot kernels in small quantities (3–4 per serving). To obtain the latter try www.vitalminerals.org

It is useful to mix the seeds in a large airtight container and sprinkle a spoonful or two onto the fruit just prior to eating. It is worth noting black onion seeds do not give off a strong onion flavour, in fact they have barely any taste at all but are recommended for their nutritional properties.

Add yoghurt as desired.

MUESLI

1 kg organic rolled oats

250 gm each rye, barley, millet flakes

50 gm each sunflower, sesame, pumpkin seeds and flaked almonds

250 gm mixed nuts (no peanuts)

100 gm pinenuts (optional)

250 gm golden sultanas and raisins (Lexias make an excellent choice)

125 gm chopped dried apricot

125 gm chopped stoned dates

125 gm chopped dried fig (optional)

125 gm desiccated coconut (optional)

There are so many excellent organic mueslis on the market these days it is hardly worth the effort to make your own. However, for anyone wanting to try their hand at making their own, this recipe has proved popular.

The amount of fruit and nuts can be varied and interchanged according to preference, as can the cereal. For example, if you do not like rye, omit it and add a little more of what you do like.

Combine all the ingredients and mix thoroughly. Store in a large airtight plastic container, or tall glass jars with well fitting lids. Wrap brown paper around the jars to keep out the light and ensure oxidation does not spoil the cereal. Store in a cool place.

The amounts given produce about 3 kg cereal which, if stored correctly, will keep for at least three months. For students this should be sufficient to last one academic term depending on how often it is eaten and the size of individual appetites!

CRUNCHY GRANOLA

(1 cup = 1 standard-size teacup)

1 cup each rolled oats, barley flakes, millet flakes, rye flakes

½ cup desiccated or flaked coconut

1 cup chopped mixed nuts (almonds, walnuts, Brazils, hazelnuts)

¼ cup each pinenuts, sunflower seeds

1 cup raisins

¼ cup organic runny honey

3 tbs organic sunflower oil

Mix the grains together.

Heat the honey and oil gently in a large pan, stirring until well combined. Turn off the heat and add the grains. Stir, ensuring the grains are well coated.

Stir in the nuts, seeds and coconut and then the fruit.

Turn out into a lightly-oiled roasting dish and bake in a slow oven (Gas 2 / 150 C) for ¾–1 hour, stirring the mixture fairly frequently to ensure a consistent roasting. If you like a dark-roasted cereal, cook for a little longer, a little less for a lighter one. Remove from the oven and allow to cool. Stir the mixture from time to time. When thoroughly cooled, transfer to a large screw top jar and store as for muesli.

This can be served with milk, fruit juice, Soya milk or yoghurt for breakfast; it makes a good snack for teenage lunch boxes, and can be sprinkled over stewed fruit and served with yoghurt for a dessert.

RAISIN PANCAKES

Makes 8 medium-sized pancakes

125 gm 85% plain flour

Pinch sea salt

1 whole egg plus 1 egg yolk

300 ml milk or Soya milk

By and large children of all ages like pancakes so these might tempt those who regularly shun breakfast.

The mixture can be made the night before for the time-pressured.

I use a small wrought iron fry pan that is dedicated solely for pancakes; it is never washed, simply wiped out with a clean cloth and stored in a cupboard. Any heavy-based fry pan will serve equally well.

Blend in a liquidiser and then add 1 tbs melted butter and whizz again. Alternatively: place flour and salt in a bowl, add the eggs and mix to a paste with as much liquid as required. Gradually add the rest of the milk, beating well with a metal spoon. Add the melted butter and mix again. If mixing the night before, be prepared for the fat to have risen to the top. Simply whizz or mix in again before cooking.

Soak 2 tbs raisins in a little apple juice or water overnight and drain in the morning.

Lightly grease the pan with butter before heating over a medium heat and cook the pancakes. The mixture will begin to bubble when the batter requires turning. Before turning add some of the raisins. Cook the pancake on the reverse side.

Serve with maple or rice syrup, or fresh yoghurt.

YOGHURT

Yoghurt comes in several varieties and consistencies and is easily obtainable from most food outlets nowadays.

Yoghurt makes a good breakfast on its own combined with a sprinkling of oatgerm, some chopped nuts, dates, figs or other dried fruit.

EGGS

Eggs are an exceptionally nutritious high protein food. Think of an egg's potential! The Chinese believe one egg provides sufficient energy for 6 people. "Go to work on an egg" was a slogan of the Egg Marketing Board, attributed to Faye Weldon, to encourage egg consumption and, for those who enjoy eggs and favour a protein as opposed to a carbohydrate start to the day, they make very versatile breakfasts.

Boiled, poached, coddled, scrambled, omelette

TO BOIL

Allow one egg per person. Add to a saucepan of boiling water and time for 4-6 minutes depending whether the yolk is to be runny or hard.

Note: eggs should not be stored in a fridge but if they are – remove to room temperature to avoid cracking when adding to boiling water.

Serve with fingers of buttered bread that can be dipped into the yolk.

Children learning to feed themselves delight in showing off their dexterity. Dipping "soldiers", like dunking ginger biscuits, often becomes a lifelong habit.

TO POACH

Allow one egg per person. Using a fry pan boil up sufficient water to cover the shelled egg. Add 1 tbs cider vinegar to prevent the egg white from streaming. Crack the egg and drop it into the water. Poach for a few minutes, a little longer for a harder yolk. A slotted spoon is useful for removing the egg. Serve on buttered wholemeal toast.

TO CODDLE

You will require an egg coddler, obtainable from the china department of good department stores. If there is a choice of size select the larger.

Bring a pan of water to the boil. Place a knob of butter and some freshly ground black pepper into the coddler. Stand this in the pan of water until the butter melts. Remove and swirl the butter, coating the sides. Crack open the egg and drop it into the coddler. Add a pinch of sea salt and / or nutmeg. Screw on the lid and immerse in the pan of water. Allow approximately 10 minutes for the egg to cook.

Serve with toast or bread and butter.

TO SCRAMBLE

Allow one to two eggs per person, whisked with a little sea salt and pepper. Place in a heavy-based, lightly-oiled saucepan, with a healthy knob of butter and 2 tbs milk or cream per egg. Stir constantly over a medium heat until the mixture begins to thicken. If you like your eggs creamy this is the time to remove from the heat, stirring because the mixture will continue to cook. For a firmer consistency cook until the solids start to separate out; you can discard the whey as you serve up the egg with a slotted spoon.

Serve on warm buttered toast.

For variety you can add ¼ tsp Dijon mustard, a dash of Worcestershire sauce or a little creamed horseradish prior to cooking.

VEGAN ALTERNATIVE: CLEONE'S TOFU SCRAMBLED EGG

Allow one packet silken tofu for two people

Turmeric

Butter

A little herb salt for seasoning

Ground black pepper

Completely drain the silken tofu. If necessary, place for a few moments on kitchen paper to absorb the remaining liquid. Thoroughly mash in a bowl and stir in some turmeric – I use 1 heaped tsp. Season. Melt a little butter in a small fry pan, tip in the tofu mixture and cook through, stirring continuously. Even egg eaters are amazed at how much this tastes like scrambled egg.

OMELETTES

Allow one or two eggs per person. For a single serving use two eggs. Whisk with a little sea salt and ground pepper plus 1 tbs water per serving. In a heavy-based fry pan, heat up sufficient olive or sunflower oil to coat the base of the pan. Add the eggs and stir around with a wooden spoon. Allow to set and fold in half with a metal spatula. Serve on a pre-heated plate.

Variations

as the mixture cooks scatter on a selection of the following:–

- 1 tsp fresh, chopped favourite herbs
- some chopped fresh tomato and basil
- a little grated cheese
- a small chopped cooked onion or a chopped raw spring onion
- 2 tbs steamed bean sprouts and a dash of tamari Soya sauce
- 2 tbs chopped cooked mushrooms
- some flaked smoked fish such as cod or haddock

BRAN MUFFINS
Makes approximately 10

Oil / grease the muffin tins

In a blender

Blend   1 breakfast cup whole milk / goat's milk / Soya milk

              1 egg

              1 tbs honey (or more according to taste)

              3 tbs cold-pressed sunflower oil

In a bowl

Mix well   1 breakfast cup plain flour

              4 tsp baking powder

              1 breakfast cup bran

              1 breakfast cup chopped dates / raisins

Add the liquid to the dry ingredients and mix together. The consistency needs to be that of a sponge cake mixture. If it is too sloppy add a little more bran, flour or some rolled oats. Divide amongst the greased muffin tins and bake (Gas 6 / 200 C) for approximately 20 minutes.

Allow to cool and serve with fresh butter and / or honey. These can be served at afternoon teatime as well as breakfast.

BREAKFAST MENU SUGGESTIONS

These suggestions are intended only as a guide, to stimulate your imagination as much as your appetite. Choose a selection from the following pages:

Monday
Carrot and apple juice
Ground rice with prunes, figs, apricots or rice syrup
Rice cakes
Baked beans on toasted rice bread *(Section Six – Bread)*
Poached eggs with or without bacon
Rice toast / rice bread with vegemite / marmite /honey / blackcurrant jam
Tea / coffee/ coffee substitute such as dandelion

Tuesday
Orange, beetroot, carrot and ginger juice
Barley flake porridge with barley malt syrup (optional)
Fruit yoghurt
Muffins
Mushroom omelette
Barley Cup

Wednesday
Millet flakes, yoghurt and seeds
Vegetarian sausage and grilled tomato
Wholemeal toast and marmalade / plum jam / pear and apple spread
Hot blackcurrant juice

Thursday
Apple juice
Compôte of dried fruit with or without ginger
Yoghurt
Scrambled eggs on toast
Rye bread / rye crispbread
Herb tea

Friday
Pear, apple, carrot and ginger juice
Porridge oats
Fried tofu and tomatoes on oatbread toast *(Section Six)*
Oatbread rolls and marmalade / maple syrup
Green tea / Rooibosch tea

Saturday
Prune juice
Granola
Sweet corn fritters
Beans on toast
Wholemeal croissants / toast and plum jam
Chai

Sunday
Cranberry juice
Fruit salad of pear, apple, plum, red grapes with seeds and yoghurt
Tofu scrambled "egg"
Kedgeree made with undyed naturally smoked flaked cod / haddock *(Section Three – Fish)*
Grilled herring / un-dyed kipper
Raisin pancakes
Home made white breadrolls *(Section Six)* / croissants / toast with marmalade / honey / malt
Banchu tea

Monday
Hot water with slice of lemon
Melon
Flaked rice and raisins soaked with rice milk
Vegetarian sausage, mushrooms and grilled tomato
Rice cakes
Toast
Lemon, Honey and Ginger tea

Tuesday
Grape juice
Flaked barley soaked with milk / Soya milk / apple juice, raisins and yoghurt
Grilled bacon or vegetarian substitute and grilled tomato
Polenta *(Section Four)*
Bread rolls / toast with marmalade / quince jelly / blackcurrant jam
Fennel tea

Wednesday
Apricot and orange juice
Yoghurt with nuts and seeds
Millet porridge / Millet croquettes *(Section Four)*
Rolls / croissants and honey
Mu Tea / Nettle tea

Thursday
Fruit juice
Fresh figs stuffed with cream cheese
Savoury pancakes *(Section One – April: Basic Pancake Mixture)* and add herbs / grated cheese /
chopped spring onions etc.
Prunes wrapped in bacon and fried egg
Ryebread
Fruit or Herb tea

Friday
Stewed apple and sultanas with fresh yoghurt
Oatmeal porridge with maple syrup and cream
Boiled eggs with oatbread fingers
Morning rolls / French bread with butter
Elderflower tea

Saturday
Apricot, apple, orange and ginger juice
Granola and yoghurt
Cornbread *(Section 6 – Bread: additions and substitutions)*
Toast and vegemite / marmite
Spearmint tea

Sunday
Hot water and lemon
Muesli with fresh nectarine and yoghurt
Pancakes with maple syrup / lemon and sugar
Granary bread, croissants, toast with honey / marmalade / cherry jam
Peppermint tea

Monday
½ Grapefruit
Cold Ground Rice (make according to packet directions with milk or Soya milk)
with sugar-free strawberry jam / fresh strawberries
Coddled eggs
Marinated herring / kipper
Rice cakes
Hibiscus tea

Tuesday
Fruit salad made of orange, kiwi fruit, mango, nectarine
Yoghurt with nuts and seeds
Smoked salmon and creamed cheese / tofu "scrambled egg"
Barley bread rolls *(Section Six)*
Lemon Balm tea

Wednesday
Strawberry and raspberry juice blended with fresh yoghurt
Muesli
Millet patties *(Section Four)*
Croissants /Toast
Fruit tea

Thursday
Pineapple juice
Nectarine / peach, mango, and grapes
Goat cheese and chive scones
Marinated herring and dill
Rye crispbread with soft goat cheese and tomato
Rooibosch tea

Friday

Tropical fruit juice made with orange, lemon, grapefruit, mango and papaya, sweetened with honey.
Rolled oats soaked with milk / oatmilk and a selection from cherries, black grapes,
nectarine, fresh apricot, peach, yoghurt and seeds
Boiled egg
Oatcakes
Dandelion coffee

Saturday

Strawberries, raspberries, redcurrants, nectarine, peach
Fresh yoghurt
Potato cakes
Poached smoked cod / haddock
Granary rolls / toast
Tea / coffee

Sunday

Apricot smoothie made with blended apricots and yoghurt
Banana
Pancakes with raspberry or strawberry puree
Vegetarian sausage, mushroom and tomato
Plain or onion omelette
Croissants, muffins, toast, plain or fruit scones
Tea / coffee / fruit tea

Monday
Bramley apple juice
Flaked rice soaked in rice milk / Soya milk / wholemilk with blackberries, and yoghurt
Beans on toast
Poppy seed / sesame seed rolls *(Section Six)*
Grain coffee

Tuesday
Pear and ginger juice
Barley porridge made from flaked barley; yoghurt and sultanas
Sliced banana on toast
Muffins / toasted pikelets
Barleycup

Wednesday
Apple, pear, ginger and carrot juice
Compôte of dried fruit, yoghurt and seeds
Millet porridge made from millet flakes, maple syrup / Demerara sugar / honey
and crème fraîche
Grilled herring
Tofu "scrambled egg" on toast
Breadrolls / cinnamon toast
Nettle tea

Thursday
Fresh pineapple / banana / blackberries
Mixed nuts and sultanas with yoghurt [optional]
Dark ryebread with Gruyere cheese and sliced tomato
Rye crispbread with soft goat's cheese and smoked salmon
Rolls made with rye flour and caraway. *(Section Six)*
Tea / coffee

Friday
Apple and blackcurrant smoothie made with fresh fruit and fresh yoghurt
Porridge with cream / crème fraîche / oatmilk
Poached egg on potato cake
Grilled bacon, black pudding, mushroom and tomato
Vegetarian sausage, mushroom and tomato
Oatcakes, oat biscuits
Hot water

Saturday
Prune juice / apricot juice
Hot stewed apple, yoghurt and seeds
Cornbread
Pancakes with blackberries and sour cream
Toast and rolls
Fennel tea

Sunday
Hot blackcurrant juice with cinnamon
Granola with yoghurt, fresh blackberries chopped red apple and fresh dates
Herb omelette with mixed mushrooms
Vegetarian sausage, tomato and tofu "scrambled egg"
Scotch pancakes
Sesame bread rolls
Toast with blackcurrant jam / redcurrant jelly
Peppermint tea

Yoga advocates balance in all areas of our life. There is much talk nowadays about a "balanced diet" and then the arguments begin as to what precisely is a balanced diet.

Yoga practice is based on harmonising Mind, Body and Spirit and the medium is the Breath. Whilst all religious traditions recognise that the Breath is sacred, even the non-religious will concede that Breath is the basis of our existence on Planet Earth. We come in on an inhalation; we exit on an exhalation: that is a fundamental fact.

The Breath also serves as a metaphor for LIFE in all its aspects inasmuch as it is an expression of the Universal Law of Expansion / Contraction. Between these two polarities exists the Pause, however infinitesimal. The Pause is the non-movement, the no-thing, the space, the silence out of which all movement, all manifestation is created. The Universe materialised out of the Void.

Harmony between the expansive and contractive pulls is regulated by the pause, the space. Healthy breathing depends upon a deeply released exhalation, followed by the pause, after which the inhalation comes in of its own accord. We need to re-educate our breathing habits, jettisoning the idea of "taking" a breath in favour of receiving it, just allowing it to come in. A natural full inhalation can only occur if we empty ourselves of the old breath (the exhalation). We require a full uptake of oxygen, not simply to live, but to ensure effective metabolism. Oxygen is required to transform the food we eat into energy. Clean-burning, energy-efficient transformation of nutrients with a minimum of residues requires we absorb the inhalation by the litre rather than the teaspoonful!

We become overweight not only through over-eating per se, or eating the "wrong" foods, but also through an inefficient processing of the food consumed. We become ill if our bodies cannot process efficiently the food we eat and toxins get stored in the intra-cellular spaces as fat. Toxins do not just produce weight gain, they can manifest in all sorts of unpleasant forms such as migraine headaches, inflamed joints and a whole host of diseases lumped together as chronic conditions. So effective breathing is a given if we are to eat well, be well and stay well.

Staying with our metaphor, eating equates with the inhalation; digestion and elimination with the exhalation and the Pause is literally the pause / space between meals. How long that pause is will depend on the individual. The snack is like a mini-meal. Some people cannot endure a resting period of four hours between meals without feeling a drop in energy (low sugar slump) so the snack will stabilise energy levels.

If we pause and listen to the body we will come to understand the signals it is giving off. To eat a snack because the body is requesting an energy top up is one thing, to eat a snack because it is 10.00 a.m. and habit dictates it is time for coffee and a biscuit to accompany it, quite another. It is also important to be able to recognise the difference between a sense of emptiness, which brings in a desire for fullness, and a slight sense of "something" missing which results in snacking for comfort. Vague feelings of something missing are often less to do with physical hunger than an indication that there is an imbalance elsewhere in our lives.

Balance or re-integration comes out of the Pause, the quiet reflection. This can take many forms from taking up a hobby to meditation. It can also come from having a good look at our diet and being honest not only about what but how we are eating. Is our relationship with our food healthy? Are we gorging, snacking out of habit, out of a sense of desperation? For some, simply eating less, allowing a decent interval to elapse between meals, will enable them to make adjustments or fine-tune other areas in their lives.

In conclusion, snacks are neither good nor bad in themselves. Some people are better for eating little and often rather than one or two large meals a day. Physically active people, teenagers, and small children constantly "on the go" are more likely to require a snack between regular meals than the elderly or those leading a more sedentary lifestyle. What we choose to snack on and why we are snacking is what will ultimately prove beneficial or detrimental to our overall wellbeing. Chocolate bars, crisps, fizzy drinks, biscuits and sweets are best reserved for a very occasional "treat" rather than regular snack foods.

SOME SUGGESTIONS FOR MID-MORNING OR MID-AFTERNOON SNACKS

Lightly-buttered plain / fruit / cheese wholemeal scone

A piece of fresh fruit – apple, banana, pear

Crispbread: – rice cakes, oatcakes, rye crispbread, wholewheat crispbread – with a choice of marmite, thin slice cheese, soft goat's cheese, nut butters, vegetarian pate, mushroom pâté, sugar-free jam

Trail mix (or any other fruit, nut and flaked coconut mixture available from health shop outlets)

Roasted nuts and seeds

Tamari-roasted sunflower seeds

Yoghurt-coated raisins

Individual small packets dried raisins (children love these in their lunch boxes)

Sesame bars

Carob bars

Grain or dried fruit bars *Note:* these usually contain palm oil (which is a saturated fat)

Mixed nuts

Nuts and raisins

Chewy dried fruit such as peaches, pears and bananas

Apple and cheese

Wholemeal sandwich made with mustard and cress and a scraping of marmite

Small pot crunchy granola

Small carton organic yoghurt – plain / fruit / naturally flavoured (e.g. vanilla)

THE PACKED LUNCH

The packed lunch conjures up an image of cheese and tomato sandwiches, packet of crisps, biscuit / piece of cake and an apple, banana or orange with, possibly for the health conscious, a carton of yoghurt. Nothing wrong with that, though we could dispense with the crisps, and if bread, yoghurt and fruit have been consumed for breakfast then it is repetitious and banal.

There is a traditionally racist joke involving the ubiquitous Englishman, Scotsman and Irishman where they are lamenting the predictability of their packed lunches. The Englishman vows that if he has been given corned beef in his sandwich once more he will jump off a cliff; the Scotsman vows the same if he is presented with haggis and the Irishman agrees that if there is cheese and onion in his lunchbox he'll join them. Needless to say they all take the big leap into Eternity. The English and Scottish wives are mortified, the Irish one bemused – she cannot understand why Paddy would do such a thing when he always made up his own lunch!

Habit is a killer: if not literally, figuratively speaking it stops the imagination dead. Those for whom lunch and sandwiches are synonymous, and who are fortunate to live in a town or city, will be blessed with a delicatessen or dedicated sandwich outlet whose combinations of fillings can seriously challenge decision making. Large numbers of customers allow for variations that would not be economic for individuals, so there is less likelihood of wastage or spoilage, and the produce is reasonably priced for the average wage-earner.

Large supermarkets also offer interesting varieties of breads and fillings which is convenient for the time-pressured. In the case of the delicatessen / sandwich shop there is the added bonus of lunch being freshly made, as opposed to pre-packed, or hustled together late the night before at home. Apart from the crisps and fizzy drinks dispenser, these outlets often have baskets of fruit-and-grain bars and a bowl of fresh fruit displayed on the counter. There are healthy alternatives, besides the water, in the chiller.

For those who prefer to make their own sandwiches, or need to provide children with a packed lunch on a regular basis, here are a few suggestions for seasonal combinations.

For the most part think about using hearty breads such as granary, rye and breads containing seeds or nuts. Use chutneys and preserves.

If cheese is a favourite:

Wensleydale with apple

Stilton with plum chutney / pear / black cherries

Cheddar and red onion steeped overnight in apple cider vinegar and a little Demerara sugar

Cream cheese and banana

Soft goats' cheese, rocket and watercress

Pâtés with avocado

Hummus with mustard-and-cress

Egg with watercress

Nut butters with black cherry jam

Nut butters with rocket, watercress

Pease pudding with cress and / or ham

Cold meats with mustards / chutneys / pickles / preserves

Smoked fish with salad leaves

Salmon / tuna with garlic mayonnaise

Smoked salmon with dill / fresh coriander

Pickled herring with cream cheese

Olives, if you like them, will combine well with cream cheeses and some hard cheeses such as Red Leicester; beef, smoked salmon, pickled herring.

SPRING

Substitute some of the dark breads with ciabatta rolls

Incorporate other varieties of fruit, such as

apricot / kiwi fruit / pineapple, with the cheese

Add more salad – there are plenty available that are not simply lettuce

Try a few dandelion leaves

SUMMER

French bread / soft white baps; wholewheat, granary or light rye loaf

Strawberries with the cream cheese or grapes, kiwi fruit and mango

Cucumber with fish

Tomato with egg

Melon / pineapple and ham

Masses of salad

Any variety of bread e.g. olive bread / sun-dried tomato bread

Use pickles, preserves, chutneys with cold meats, eggs, fish or cheese

Cooked, de-husked sweet corn with cream cheese / tuna / salmon

Pear, stem ginger and soft goat's cheese

Banana and goat's cheese / peanut butter

Nut butters; pâtés; pease pudding; all go well with salads

Hummus and mango / avocado / watercress

ALTERNATIVES TO THE SANDWICH

Kitchenware nowadays is both versatile and ingeniously designed. Containers manufactured from light, durable materials come in all colours, shapes and sizes, are easily stacked or stored and have largely replaced the traditional sandwich box. Packaging affects our visual sense – if the container is aesthetically pleasing the appetite is whetted and we are prepared for lunch. A particular coloured lid on an opaque base could determine a sense of eagerness or indifference towards the meal in hand.

Texture is also important since it affects the sense of touch. Whether we like a rough surface, as opposed to a smooth one, a hard brittle plastic or a softer more pliable container, a curved base that sits in the palm of the hand or a rectangular base that is more comfortable on a table top or a lap – all these factors influence our relationship with our food on some level, either consciously or unconsciously. Next comes our sense of smell – as we lift the lid we instantly sense whether the food is fresh or stale.

Manufactured foods are cleverly disguised to fool our intrinsic senses but the more sensitive we become to our engagement with our food the more selective we will be about what we put in our mouths. The more we dispense with old habits (such as eating for eating's sake, because it is "time" to eat, or whilst engaged on another activity altogether such as reading or watching TV) the more likely we are to feed ourselves. Our noses will become attuned like sniffer dogs to the saturation of salt, sugar and hydrogenated fat.

Without necessarily being able to identify individual additives, an overall sense is created that somehow what is on offer is not quite wholesome. To make a point, I used to suggest to my cookery students that the packet would probably be more nutritious than the processed cereal contents; the reasoning being that the cardboard was possibly closer than the cereal to its state of origin.

And finally we taste and eat lunch. Since the senses of taste and smell are so closely inter-linked, what we taste will instantly confirm what we have smelled. So if we are actively engaged with our food, its composition, preparation, its freshness, we will not become deluded or dulled, equating with the equivalent of food processing plants. Instead, like the food, we will stay fresh, alert and energised.

SUGGESTIONS FOR THE SEASONAL PACKED LUNCH

Small flask hot soup: lentil / mixed root vegetable /
celery and stilton /
parsnip and apple, pea and ham; barley

Granary bread roll, slices of dark rye bread

Wedge of cold Spanish Omelette

Quiche

Small cubes hard goat / sheep cheese with herb salad
leaves

Pease pudding / polenta / hummus with salad of cold
potato, beetroot,
celery, watercress, and coleslaw

Small pot of mixed nuts / fruit and nuts / raisins

Small pot Brazil nuts

Small pot mixed dried / crystallised fruits: pineapple,
ginger, coconut,
sultanas, peaches/ pears

Fresh fruit

Figs / prunes / dates stuffed with cream cheese and or
stem ginger.

Piece of reduced-sugar fruitcake

SPRING

Small flask clear soup: celery, leek, onion, nettle

Crispbread / light bread roll

Cold hard boiled eggs / curried eggs / creamed eggs with watercress, rocket, salad leaves

Polenta / hummus with cold potato and celery

Rice Salad *(Section One – August)*

Small cubes of waxy cheese (Edam / Gruyere / mozzarella) with watercress,
celery and / or beetroot mixed with yoghurt / sour cream

Rice and corn salad

Small pots of mixed nuts / fruit and nuts / dried mixed fruit

Banana / apple / pear

Grain and fruit bar

Chewy dried fruit bar

Piece of rice cake / carrot cake

SUMMER

Small flask cold soup / consommé, French bread / ciabatta

Any combination of green salads, plain / dressed with
French dressing / light oil-and-lemon dressing

Eggs with tomato, cucumber, celery

Cubes of cheese, olives, cherry tomatoes, pickled beetroot, raita (cucumber soaked in plain
yoghurt and sea salt)

Grated carrot, desiccated coconut and raisins with small cubes hard or waxy cheese

Stilton cheese with celery and apple salad

Stuffed avocado with coleslaw / mixed salad (include rocket and coriander)

Tofu burger with green salad or tomato salad

Shredded cold, cooked fresh tuna steak with tomato salad

Herb salad with cheese cubes / pickled herring / smoked fish flaked / small chunks ham

Tropical fruit salad

Fresh strawberries / raspberries / redcurrants / cherries / grapes / melon,
peach / nectarine / kiwi fruit / mango

Chocolate / lemon / coffee mousse

Small wedge lemon citron tarte

AUTUMN

Small flask creamy soup with bread roll / rye bread / melba toast *(Section Four)*

Fish tarte *(Section Three)* / small chunks of cooked fresh tuna steak / pickled herring with coleslaw or green salad

Wedge Spanish style omelette made with ham and onion

Quiche

Smoked tofu cubed in a large mixed, green salad, lemon and oil dressing. topped with a few croutons

Mushroom Croustade *(Section One – June)*

Potato salad; beetroot; celery, apple, raisin and walnut salad

Coleslaw

Wensleydale / Derby / Stilton / Lancashire / Cheshire cheese cubes

Grated Cheddar with shredded carrot, apple and raisin

Blackberries / apple / pear / plums / orange / tangerine / banana

Mixed fruit and nuts / almonds / hazelnuts or cobnuts / tamari-roasted sunflower seeds

Mixed salad and nasturtium flower heads stuffed with cream cheese

Dates stuffed with cream cheese / Figs stuffed with soft goat's cheese

Muesli bar

Small pot crunchy granola

Small pot mixed seeds: pumpkin, sunflower, sesame

Chewy fruit bar

Piece carrot, rice, or seed cake

Ideally drinks should not be consumed with a meal but taken about half an hour beforehand or up to two hours after. This is to ensure that the digestive function is not impaired through over dilution of the gastric juices. However, food has become more than simply a matter of survival in our society; it has taken on all manner of social overtones, and in some cases what, where and how we eat is a defining statement in itself.

To be seen around carrying a bottle of branded water is currently de rigeur. It used to be Lucozade! Out shopping we meet up with friends for a coffee, and usually something to eat with it. A cup of coffee rounds off dinner, and wine accompanies it. To deny ourselves these fads and rituals altogether in order to follow an exact dietary regime may well purify the body, and make us feel righteous, but at what cost? Starving the soul? Yoga is about acquiring balance, which should allow us to follow custom and at the same time be aware of our own body needs. If we overindulge, we may need to readjust the life-style until equilibrium is restored.

At one time, fasting was common practice and still is in some cultures. The weekly short fast or abstention meant resting the body, giving it space to clean up and put its house back in order. Fasting between seasons allows the body to readjust and prepare for dietary changes. It was customary to abstain from food whilst drinking only water for one or several days but nowadays our bodies are so full of environmental toxins it would be advisable to consult a medical practitioner before embarking wholly on a water fast for longer than a day. It would be safer to fast on steamed wholegrain rice, permitting toxins to be absorbed and eliminated via the gut rather than releasing directly into the bloodstream and resulting in toxic overload.

In striving for balance we are looking for harmony on all levels of our being or existence. Ease not dis-ease is our natural state. To be aware is to be conscious. Yoga is not just a physical practice, it requires mental commitment equally. Clear, un-muddled mental faculties allow us to make conscious, rational choices about our lives. An alert, lively, inquiring mind allows us to be, and stay, informed so whilst indulging in a little cappuccino and delicate fairy cake, it may be worth reminding ourselves of what our bodies need not just for maintenance but also for survival.

The human body is composed mostly of fluids that, amongst other functions, excrete waste products or toxins via urine, perspiration and exhalation. Replacing these fluids is essential to prevent dehydration and thirst is the body's reminder for us to take a drink in order to re-hydrate, with water. Ideally water should be taken apart from food and drunk or sipped regularly throughout the day. This will ensure that the body cells are constantly flushed, and reduce the likelihood of build up of debris. A clear, fresh complexion, smooth skin and sparkling eyes are all signs of healthy body cells and drinking ample amounts of fresh water will help to ensure or maintain this.

In Britain water is an amenity we take for granted: it is, literally, on tap in every household and we can drink it without fear of being poisoned. From an historical perspective this is a relatively recent innovation because until we became aware that fatal diseases such as cholera were directly attributed to polluted water, it was commonplace to throw household refuse into the streets where it was washed away down the runnels and into the rivers. Rivers are the arteries of the planet and when polluted with waste products, they suffer the equivalent of blood poisoning in a human.

Small wonder people living in the Middle-Ages learned not to drink water directly; instead they drank ale or small beer, and this was probably the norm until an expanding British Empire introduced us to the exotic novelties of tea, coffee and cocoa. Interestingly, in the eighteenth century chocolate was drunk unsweetened and made with water whereas today hot chocolate is invariably made with frothed milk and sugared.

The immediate post-Second World War generation was probably raised mainly on water and tea. Tea and coffee, usually consumed with milk and maybe sugar, have overtaken cocoa or chocolate as the nation's beverages of preference but whilst appealing to the palette neither actually satisfies the body's requirement for water. Many people are surprised to learn both tea and coffee will tend to dehydrate the body, rather than replenish its fluid requirements, but it is worth remembering the milk and sugar accompaniments are foods that require fluids for digestion!

Coffee became the favoured drink amongst teenagers from the late 1950s onwards and on the back of that came the cola drinks and all the variants. The fizzy drinks industry boomed once refrigerators, and then chiller cabinets in every corner shop, became commonplace. These beverages are coloured, flavoured, sweetened, carbonated water. It has been estimated that a can of fizzy drink contains up to 8 teaspoons of sugar. The diet varieties, whilst dispensing with the sugar simply substitute with aspartame. The chill and fizz act like an anaesthetic inasmuch as we do not taste the sweetness to the degree we would without them. A bottle of warm, flat lemonade is considered unpalatable.

Cordial concentrates are also popular: heavily sweetened and coloured, many came to be linked with hyperactivity in children because of the ubiquitous use of tartrazine. With the compulsory labelling of food in the 1980s many suspect additives were dispensed with or substituted but the sugar content remained unaltered for the most part. Excess sugar will not only dehydrate the body it will also de-mineralise it through the body's effort to digest and remove it from the system. **(Section Seven – SUGAR).**

So whilst the occasional use of cordial or canned drink will do no harm, liberally incorporating them into the daily diet could cause long term health problems.

In the 1950s many Europeans living in East Africa were privileged to have water connected to the house but because of all the environmental pathogens such as bilharzia we never drank it directly from the tap: it was boiled and then filtered, and when refrigerators were introduced, chilled. During a furlough in England I recall amazement at my grandmother drawing a glass of water for me from her kitchen tap. It was February, freezing cold, and I was five years old. Though I have tried, over the years, to recapture that first experience of ice-cold Yorkshire tap water, I have never tasted water like that again. It was pure nectar.

Not all tap water tastes clean on the palette. There should be no metallic "after" taste. The water companies treat our water with chemicals in order to ensure its safety but this does not necessarily mean it is healthy. In some areas water has a flat, rather than a vibrant taste, and I have even seen scum residues surfacing on a cup of tea. This could account for some of the popularity of bottled waters though there is concern about artificial oestrogen in the plastic containers leaching into the water.

One way to minimize the health risk is to render tap water palatable by boiling it in a large open stainless steel or enamelled pan. This gets rid of the chlorine though it will not remove fluoride. I use a container that holds 10 pints. After a few minutes rapid boiling, turn off the heat, cover with a lid, and cool. If you like your water ice cold it can then be stored in glass bottles or jugs in a refrigerator.

A glass of hot or warm water first thing in the morning will stimulate the body and actively assist in the elimination process.

Cider Vinegar will help to alkalise the system. 1 tbs in a glass of hot water. If this is too sharp sweeten with a little honey or small amount of organic blackcurrant cordial.

Herbal Teas which are calming to the system

Many herbal and fruit teas are produced commercially and sold through supermarket chains as well as specialist health shops. The advantage of health shops is that they tend to stock the raw herbs and you can make your own combinations.

The Complete Book of Herbs and Spices by Claire Loewënfeld and Philippa Back is excellent – for its illustrations, comprehensive descriptions and uses of herbs, as well as for its charts at the back, one of which is for herb teas. This chart not only names the herb, indicates the parts used, gives specific directions on how to brew and take it, but also lists the applications and effects.

Caraway - a tea made from the seeds is excellent for digestive and bowel complaints. Children tend to like the flavour.

Chamomile – this is excellent for fretful babies, particularly when teething; over-excitement in children; and to aid sleep. Make an infusion of the dried flowers.

Dill – infuse the leaves for a flavoursome drink. It will aid digestion and stomach aches, aid sleep and stimulate milk production in nursing mothers. It was the predominant flavour in a prescriptive colic remedy for infants.

Fennel – aids digestion and calms. It is said to accelerate the digestion of oily foods. The seeds benefit the eyes and an infusion can make a soothing eye lotion.

Fenugreek – a strong tea made from the seeds can aid digestive problems; for fevers add a little lemon and honey.

Ginger – boil the root thinly sliced in a pan of water. This can be combined with fruit juices such as apple, orange or lemon and a little honey.

Lemon Balm – promotes relaxation and sleep.

Lemon verbena – is a sedative, digestive tonic and calms the nervous system.

Liquorice – drunk cold, this tea soothes the guts or alimentary canal, has a pain killing effect on stomach ulcers, and can act as a mild laxative.

Alternatives to Black Tea And Coffee

Green Tea - drunk regularly, is said to reduce the risk of some cancers in both men and women, notably prostate and breast cancers. It will lower blood pressure levels so it has also been linked with a reduced risk of stroke and heart disease. It should be remembered, however, that nothing acts in isolation as a "magic bullet" and the whole dietary regime may require overhauling when looking at patterns of dis-ease. It is a fallacy to think we can gorge on junk foods and substitute the usual cup of tea with green tea and be "safe" from some external invader when the real breakdown of health originates from within. It is also a fallacy that wholesome diet alone can preserve our health, though it will provide a good physical base for developing our human potential, and minimise the risks of breakdown along our journey through Life.

Gunpowder Tea
Mu tea contains a mixture of herbs including ginseng.

Decaffeinated Coffees are quite popular with those wanting to reduce their caffeine intake but it is worth looking at how the caffeine has been extracted – by a steam or chemical process. There is some concern that chemical residues left in the coffee could be more harmful than the caffeine in the long term. Extracting the caffeine by steam does not present this problem.

Coffee Alternatives are probably best considered drinks in their own right than substitutes to avoid disappointment. They are made from a variety of ingredients such as dandelion, fig, barley malt and chicory and can be found widely available in Health outlets.

Symmington's Dandelion Coffee is particularly flavoursome without the bitterness that can be associated with dandelion root.

Barley Cup is relaxing.

SECTION THREE
Meat, Fish and Poultry

MEAT

Whether we eat or abstain from eating meat, fish or poultry is a personal, cultural or religious decision rather than a moral judgment about right and wrong. I have known vegetarians and vegans who could not contemplate eating meat for aesthetic reasons, others who decline on health grounds, and yet others who state they are simply not suited to a meat-based diet. I have known a few who feel morally superior by abstaining from eating meat, and still others who feel obliged to become vegetarians upon taking up yoga, as if this was a prerequisite when in fact it isn't. Vegetarianism is not synonymous with spirituality any more than eating meat renders you insensitive to other sentient beings living on this planet.

Many people who practise yoga adopt a vegetarian diet for either philosophical or practical reasons. Meat consumption can lead to a feeling of heaviness in some practitioners so the vegetarian alternative would make sense. Physical practice is best done at least two and preferably four hours after eating food from whatever source, but you do not have to be an adept to benefit from a few gentle stretches to keep you supple and the waistline trim.

For a variety of reasons people may experiment with vegetarianism and eventually revert to including some meat, fish or poultry in their diet. Not all people are suited to a strict vegetarian regime; they become ill if they cannot absorb sufficient nutrients from grains, nuts and pulses or if they do not vary the diet adequately.

My own daughter eventually fell into the latter category some years after embracing vegetarianism at the age of twelve, which is not uncommon amongst young girls. It was spring, when new-born lambs were bucking and frolicking in the Northumberland countryside, and a chance remark from her father made her connect the tiny ecstatic creatures with the roast that would be appearing on her plate once we rounded the next corner to the village pub. Sixteen years later and she still declines meat though she does eat a little fish on the advice of her health practitioner.

A concern in the first instance was that she was "difficult" to feed anyway. As a small child she disliked vegetables in any shape or form bar potatoes and for a long time her diet seemed to consist almost entirely of Pizza Margarita and chocolate. Yet despite my fretting and clucking, she survived. Which just goes to prove there is more to human diet than the sum of its physical constituents.

At one time, when resources were scarce, we ate what we could get hold of and were grateful for it. Nowadays with endless choices passed before us we can afford to be particular and enjoy the luxury of option. Whether we have retained our forebears' sense of gratitude remains questionable. But whatever we consume, be it animal or vegetable, requires appreciation, if only to retain an awareness of the sanctity and mortality of all Life on this plane of existence. We do not have to be religious or spiritual to be thankful. Saying "Grace" before meals was one way of reminding us that what we were about to receive was responsible for our continuance, and on some level kept us humble. Without humility we are in danger of becoming arrogant and selfish. It also, albeit subconsciously, attuned us to our own inevitable mortality. And death is a taboo subject for most of us living in the West.

Africa was a great educator in life and death. Reality was stark: death stared you in the face no matter which way you turned, and life was possibly the more precious for that. When I lived in Tanzania feline predators were not confined to game parks. At night Africans travelling on foot were at risk from the odd rogue lion or leopard. At six years old I lost a favourite playmate to infection after what had appeared a straightforward appendectomy; I lost another to a crocodile at ten. From what I remember, African children with bloated bellies and stick-thin arms and legs were not an uncommon sight even when there was no famine. My memory in this instance may be faulty to a degree but certainly European children were the better nourished.

In the absence of a sanitised modern supermarket or specialist butcher's shop, dinner was the undisguised consequence of animal slaughter and in the case of chickens, foretold by the addition of sound effects. Meat was bought in the open, fly-infested market. It was invariably tough, stringy, barely digestible and often unpalatable unless stewed for hours, curried, or ingeniously reinvented with culinary additives known only to Mpishi (Swahili for cook). Forget tenderised beef, it was more like cowhide. Lamb was non-existent, mutton a luxury. All too often it was goat and old goat at that. So it is unsurprising that most households supplemented their bought meat with home-raised chickens. I say chickens guardedly for these feathered parodies would have had the average corn-fed British bantam on its back, hysterical with derision. The one saving grace was pork, preserve of the White Fathers who raised pigs with the dedication of mediaeval Benedictines and thereby spared many a European molar from utter ruination.

Fish was a rarity if you lived inland, unless you knew how to by-pass the system, which my father did when we lived in Tabora. Part of his work within the medical service gave him connections with Kigoma, a township situated on Lake Tanganyika. Ice-packed vacuum flasks containing supplies of vaccines or other medications would travel down-line by train, only to be returned crammed with ice-packed lakeside fish. It was delicious. Authority was either ignorant of or blind to the practice but I am certain my father was not alone in flouting Colonial Service rules and regulations. Too many civil servants enjoyed the luxury of fresh fish to make a fuss or complaint. Besides, so long as no one is hurt in the process a little deviancy now and then re-ignites the mischief we enjoyed as children and warms the spirit.

Presumably some people ate game. I do not recall wild buck or warthog appearing on the menu but I do remember rabbit.

A farm on the outskirts of one particular township raised turkeys and bred rabbits. These were the cuddly kind, the sort to be found in any UK pet shop. Smitten, I wanted one for keeps whereas my father's interest was of a more prandial nature. In the end there was a compromise, rabbits would be bought for the table and I could choose one to live alongside the dog, goat, rescued duck, and those hens kept for laying.

In due course only the black and white rabbit remained and, finding chickens somewhat dull companions, began absconding, to the chagrin of the Shamba Boy, our gardener, on whom fell the task of search and rescue. I am not sure what caused him the most grief, my tearful pleading that poor Fluff had escaped yet again and must be found immediately, or catching the creature once he had been located.

Inevitably the day dawned when the rabbit could not be traced. I was upset, the gardener evasive, and when I was insistent that the search be continued, my father's patience snapped. Fluff, I was told, was the meat in the pie being served for lunch.

Recently, alongside the novelties of ostrich and even crocodile, rabbit meat has been re-appearing on the British market but, to this day, I could not contemplate eating rabbits; even the tiresome ones that proliferate North Northumberland and every one of them related to Bugs Bunny.

Preferences aside, the pre-eminent question that needs answering has to be is it safe to eat? In Africa the meat might have been tough and even the source of an occasional tummy upset but we were not in danger of brain damage. It came without chemicals, colourings or potentially toxic residues of growth promoters and routinely administered antibiotic that is common practice in British farming today.

This is a complicated and controversial subject but I firmly believe organic meat is healthier than meat obtained from intensively reared animals, not only because they will not have been subjected to the above, but they will be less stressed for having had a natural diet and freedom to roam. It has to be said, however, that some good quality non-organic beef cattle benefit from a free-range grass-fed existence as well. The fat laid down in the tissues of free-range cattle differs from that of intensively reared ones. The Nuffield Institute of Comparative Medicine demonstrated in the 1970s that free-range beef cattle lay down saturated adipose fats and polyunsaturated structural fats in the proportion of one part to three. In intensively reared animals these proportions are reversed.

At one time animals were slaughtered locally or on the farm in Britain. Nowadays, in order to satisfy modern safety standards and health requirements they are subjected to long journeys to centralised abattoirs. This can be highly stressful for animals that may well sense their impending fate and become even more terrified whilst waiting to be "processed".

In the final analysis it is worth noting that food is energy and energy is transferable. In the same way that a stormy sea produces different waves from a calm one, fear vibrates at a different frequency from contentment. On an intrinsic level the energy derived from a stressed, terrified animal will differ radically from that of a contented one.

As we have become more aware of ethical sustainability in all areas of farming, a demand for locally produced meat, as well as for free-range and organically reared animals, is growing. Whilst there may be no way round the centralised abattoir for the moment, at least animals raised as naturally as possible will enjoy a relatively carefree life. Many people who switch to organic produce affirm that the meat also has a better flavour or texture.

All varieties of meat are highly concentrated complete protein foods and, however delicious they may taste to the connoisseur, adults require only small amounts for optimum health, mostly for repair of tissue and not for growth. For many people one of the deterrents to buying organic meat is the comparative extra cost. However, if quality becomes the paramount consideration when determining our diet, maybe reducing the quantity or eating meat less frequently will overcome the problem.

Our bodies are designed to absorb and utilise nutrients for growth, repair and sustenance, and to eliminate surpluses to requirements. Proteins are mostly composed of nitrogen that is broken down and eliminated by the kidneys as uric acid. Overworking the kidneys on a regular basis will eventually result in exhaustion and possible debility. If you like to eat steak everyday, fine – but how much at any one time is just as important as how often.

Appetites vary with individuals: someone with a large appetite who balances his / her protein intake with an equally large intake of fresh fruit and vegetables can be as healthy as one with a smaller meat intake; or someone who eats meat occasionally or yet another who abstains altogether. It may be that we go through a phase of wanting a particular food on a regular basis for a period of time only to find that sometime afterwards we want it only occasionally or we might "go off it" altogether.

An acquaintance had been dedicated to vegetarianism for fifteen years when she developed a desire for fish. Being somewhat strong-willed, she resisted the urge for about two years, until she developed signs of anaemia and the desire became a craving that would not be gainsaid. Her first visit to the fish shop resulted in her emerging with two very large pieces of battered cod. After fastidiously removing the batter, she downed both pieces in minutes and with absolute relish.

This pattern was repeated on a daily basis for about three weeks after which she began to space her fish shop visits to once every three days and then once a week. She still eats fish on a fairly regular basis but not de-battered cod. At the time her partner was convinced she had shares in North Shields Fish Market and she was teased mercilessly about an ability to deplete the nation's dwindling cod stocks all on her own.

Mirth aside, this was a clear sign from her body that her diet was deficient in the nutrients it required. We have this naïve supposition that intelligence is lodged in the brain, in particular the intellect, when the brain is just an aspect of the entire nervous system. The intellect is only the most recently developed part of the brain. Intelligence is housed in every single body cell, like a hologram, and body wisdom is ignored at one's peril. Yoga practice, which does not necessarily equate with physical exercise, as it is generally perceived, re-tunes us.

During our practice, by focusing attention moment by moment on sensations and signals emanating from the body, we gradually become aware of its wisdom and learn to reintegrate this with what we know intellectually. This way we learn to "know our self" which is a pre-requisite for truly learning to understand our fellows without feeling compelled to judge them.

This section includes some recipes that have been approved by meat-eating friends, and will be variations on a theme familiar to most people who eat meat as a matter of course. Meat, fish and poultry that lend themselves to a variety of cooking techniques from poaching, braising, and grilling, to stewing, boiling, or roasting are highly versatile foods.

LAMB

MUTTON AND POTATO BAKE
Serves 6-8

1½ kg cooked shoulder / leg mutton, sliced. Goat meat (Chevon) can be substituted for mutton

1 large onion thickly sliced

3 leeks thickly sliced

1 kg potatoes peeled and sliced

1 heaped tbs plain 85% flour

Sea salt and pepper

1 tbs ghee or olive oil / sunflower oil

50 gm melted butter

500 ml stock or 350 ml stock + 150 ml dry white wine

1 bay leaf

Few sprigs chopped fresh lemon / common thyme

Heat the ghee or oil in a large fry pan and soften the onions and leeks over a low heat. Stir in the flour and slowly add the stock / wine, stirring until thickened. Turn off the heat. Season with sea salt and pepper. Stir in the herbs.

In a deep casserole layer the meat, leeks and cooked onions. Cover with the sliced potato. Pour over the melted butter evenly and bake in a pre-heated oven (Gas 6 / 200 C) for 1 hour or until the potato yields to the point of a knife.

Accompaniments:

Winter
Serve with carrots, mashed swede, diced young turnips and Brussels sprouts.

Spring
Serve with whole baby carrots, creamed butternut, green cabbage dredged with lemon juice and caraway seeds.

Summer
I would not serve this dish in the summer – it is too heavy.

Autumn
Serve with mashed pumpkin, curly kale / cabbage, sweet corn.

Alternatively, a large bowl of creamed spinach with a light grating of nutmeg.

KIDNEYS AND CIDER
Serves 6-8

8–10 lambs' kidneys

2 tbs ghee and 1 tbs sunflower oil

1 onion finely chopped

125 gm button mushrooms quartered

1 heaped tbs plain 85% flour

2 tbs Dijon mustard

175 ml crème fraîche or double cream

500 ml dry cider, approximately

Sea salt and freshly ground black pepper

Handful snipped chives for garnish

Skin and cut the kidneys into 3 or 4 pieces discarding any fat. Remove the central core by cutting a V-shape from the centre of each kidney.

Melt the ghee with the oil in a large fry pan. Add the kidneys, sauté over a high heat for approximately 3–4 minutes, stirring frequently until well browned, then transfer onto a plate using a slotted spoon.

Add the onion and mushrooms to the pan and sauté for a few minutes until softened. Stir in the flour and then gradually add the cider, stirring continuously until you obtain a thick sauce.

Blend in the cream and then stir in the mustard and seasoning.

Add the kidneys and cook for a few minutes.

Transfer to a pre-heated serving dish and scatter the chives over the top just prior to serving.

Accompany with a bowl of brown rice and a mixed salad, or green beans, minted fresh peas, broad beans.

ROAST LAMB WITH APRICOTS

½ shoulder or 1 shoulder lamb depending on whether it is to serve 4 / 8

A handful washed dried apricots, sufficient to line the flap

A few sprigs fresh rosemary (optional)

1 clove garlic

Sea-salt and freshly ground black pepper

1 large piece of tinfoil, sufficient to wrap around the entire joint

Set the oven to its highest setting.

Wipe the lamb with a clean damp cloth and place on the tinfoil.

Lift the flap and, if necessary, use a sharp knife to deepen it; insert the apricots underneath. Sneak in the clove of garlic unpeeled.

Generously salt and then grind some black pepper over the surface.

Wrap the tinfoil securely around the joint and place on the tray of a roasting dish so that any escaping juices can drip into the roasting pan.

Place in the oven at its highest setting and cook for ½ an hour. Then turn the heat down to the lowest setting and leave for approximately 4 hours. If using a whole shoulder then allow 6 hours.

Remove from the oven and drain the juice, keeping the meat warm on a pre-heated serving dish while you make the gravy.

To make the gravy, reduce the meat liquid to half. Pour this into a small saucepan, add a little sherry and, if necessary, a sprinkling of dry meat stock. A tsp redcurrant jelly blended in is also good.

Alternatively, thicken the juices with a little slaked arrowroot. Bring to the boil, stirring, and check for seasoning. If more gravy is required add vegetable stock or water.

Serve at once with a selection of seasonal vegetables.

The meat will literally fall away from the bone. I serve it in pieces rather than in slices.

Accompaniments:

Winter
Roast potatoes, roast parsnips and carrots, mashed swede, dark green buttered cabbage, steamed leeks.

Spring
Minted new potatoes, boiled / roasted onions, steamed celery, and broccoli.

Summer
Rice, broad beans, peas, large green leafy salad

Autumn
Creamed potato, mashed butternut with nutmeg, and a medley of roasted vegetables – courgette, red onion, pumpkin, red pepper, carrot, tomato, leeks, and cauliflower.

BEEF

Brisket can also be cooked successfully by the above method.

Omit the apricots and rosemary.

Instead, smear the surface generously with horseradish cream or mustard.

If the joint is very lean place a walnut sized knob of ghee / suet / dripping on the upper surface prior to foil wrapping.

Beef is more robust than lamb and takes particularly well to roasted vegetables for balance.

FOR A CLASSIC ROAST

Use Sirloin or Fore Rib.

Sometimes I omit the horseradish from the beef and use it to cream mashed potatoes instead.

Accompaniments:
Instead of creamed mashed potatoes try potatoes baked in cream; roasted butternut or pumpkin; roasted onion and braised celery; lots of boiled dark green cabbage or kale enriched with a knob of butter

POT ROAST

Joint of brisket

Generous quantities of onions, leeks thickly sliced and a variety of root vegetables such as carrots, white turnip, swede chunked. Omit potato.

Sea salt and black pepper; 1 bouquet garni; 1 - 2 bay leaves

Meat or vegetable stock sufficient to cover the meat

A little ghee / dripping / olive oil

In a large saucepan, or a casserole that can be used on the top of a hob, heat the fat / oil and add the brisket, turning on all sides to seal in the juices.

Turn down the heat and set the meat onto a plate.

Sauté the onions, leeks and chopped root vegetables for a few minutes.

Return the meat to the pan and liberally cover with stock.

Add the bouquet garni and bay leaf.

Season and bring rapidly to the boil for a few minutes.

Turn down to the lowest setting, cover and slowly cook for up to four hours.

DUMPLINGS

Dumplings, particularly in the absence of potato, make an excellent accompaniment alongside green cabbage.

For the dumplings use twice the amount of SR flour to fat. Shredded suet is good. I tend to use butter / vegetarian suet because I use dumplings mostly in vegetarian cooking. Season with sea salt.

Add some mixed dried or fresh herbs for variation.

Rub the fat and flour as for pastry crumbs and mix with sufficient cold water to obtain a workable dough.

Divide into small balls and add to the brisket and vegetables 20 minutes prior to serving.

VEAL

Organic veal ensures the calf has been reared with its mother. Otherwise it may come from one that has been removed from her a few days after birth, causing both animals' enormous distress and needless suffering.

Veal steaks are best pan-fried to seal in their flavour.

PORK

Pig meat is the greasiest or richest of the meats in common usage.

In New Zealand pork is particularly favoured amongst the Maoris, where it would have been a staple food prior to the arrival of the Pakehas (Europeans) and the introduction of sheep. Many Maoris favour the richness of pork accompanied by roasted kumara (sweet potato).

We lived on the East coast of the North Island where the Maori population was significant. On one occasion we were privileged to be invited onto a Marae where dinner was cooked in a hangi. This is a centuries-old method of cooking in a pit. The prepared food is placed in flax baskets, wrapped in wet sacks which are then lowered onto hot stones and buried under sods of earth. Several hours later the food is exhumed and served up as a communal banquet. This method of cooking imparts a delicate smoky flavour to the food. Traditionally wild pig was used though nowadays this is mainly reserved for special feasts such as the tangi.

The event was memorable, not just for the mouth-wateringly delicious food, but the ceremonial, the dignity, and the jovial company made the entire event a kind of sacrament.

Without taking anything away from that particular occasion, the nearest equivalent that comes to mind is a gathering of friends around the barbecue. There is something incomparable with eating outdoors, a faint lingering throw-back to our earliest relatives which we delight in reviving from time to time, weather permitting!

In this country during the Middle-Ages wild boar roamed our forests and woodlands and was the preserve of the king and nobility; and the Boar's head, complete with orange-stuffed mouth, possibly the centrepiece of the banqueting table. Wild pig meat is darker coloured and leaner textured than farmed pork and it has a stronger, less rich flavour. To combat some of the richness it is common practice to combine or accompany the meat with fruits such as apple, citrus or pineapple whose acidity or enzymes will help break up the fat during digestion. For example:

- Roast pork and apple sauce
- Pork chops dredged in orange or lemon juice
- Gammon and pineapple

PORK KEBABS FOR A BARBECUE

Use lean meat such as pork fillet and allow between 750 gm–1 kg for 8 people.

Small onions or shallots

Pineapple chunks

4 large beefsteak tomatoes

For the marinade

Mix together in a bowl

2 tbs tamari sauce

1 tbs tomato puree

1 tbs runny honey

1 tsp Dijon mustard

1 tbs orange / pineapple juice

1" finely chopped peeled root ginger

Cut the pork into cubes, place in the marinade and coat thoroughly. Leave for ½ an hour.

Remove the meat from the marinade and place on kitchen paper to drain. Skewer, alternating with onion and pineapple and grill on the barbecue.

For variety add chunks of courgette, aubergine.

Slice the tomatoes crosswise. Sprinkle with sea salt and pepper and grill alongside the kebabs.

Accompany with a variety of salads such as:

Shredded carrot, raisin and coconut

Potato salad

Rice salad (Section 1– August)

Coleslaw

Sliced peppers and mango

Mixed green leaves with rocket

Small side-dishes or bowls of pickled beetroot, apple sauce, guacamole

For flavour and safety I use only free-range, organically fed poultry which is now widely available. Wild fowl such as partridge, woodcock or pheasant is available locally in Northumberland, as is duck, which is smaller and leaner than farmed ducks. Farmers' markets are other possible outlets for free-range poultry.

DUCK BREASTS IN ORANGE SAUCE

Allow 1 duck breast per person

1 onion finely chopped

1–2 cloves garlic crushed

1 tbs sweet sherry and ½ glass red wine

1 tbs freshly chopped parsley

1 tbs ghee or olive oil

1 heaped tbs organic 85% plain flour, or organic plain white flour seasoned with sea-salt and freshly ground black pepper.

Juice of 2 oranges or 1 glass organic orange juice

1 tbs vegetable purée and ½ glass vegetable stock

1 tbs crème fraîche (optional)

Skin the duck and coat generously in the flour.

Heat the ghee / olive oil in a large fry pan and lightly fry the duck breasts on both sides to seal in the juices (5 minutes). Transfer onto a plate.

Reduce the heat and fry the onion and garlic until translucent. Add the purée, sherry and red wine and blend. Replace the duck and cook for 10 minutes. stirring to allow the sauce to thicken. Add ½ the parsley, vegetable stock and sufficient orange juice to cover the duck. Cover and simmer for 45–60 minutes. or until the duck feels tender to the point of a knife.

Turn into a large pre-heated dish and keep warm. Just prior to serving, sprinkle with the remaining parsley and stir in the crème fraîche, if using.

Accompaniments:

A large bowl of mashed potato – creamed with butter and a generous amount of single cream; baby carrots; Brussels sprouts in season / broccoli; minted peas

DIANNE'S LEMON CHICKEN
For up to 8 people

1½ tbs ghee or butter

1 free-range chicken breast per person

2 tbs dry sherry

3 tbs dry white wine

Zest of 1 lemon

1½ tbs lemon juice

¼ pt. each single and double cream

300 gm Gruyere cheese grated

Sea-salt and ground pepper

Fry the chicken in ghee or butter for 5 mins and then transfer to a roasting or baking tin.

Add the sherry, wine, zest, juice and seasoning to the juices in the pan and blend.

Remove from the heat, add the cream, stir and pour over the chicken. Sprinkle with the Gruyere cheese and cook in the oven (Gas 4 / 180 C) for 35 minutes. Check the seasoning and serve immediately.

Accompaniments:
Potato croquettes; creamed parsnips; leeks; a bowl of green salad dredged in lemon juice and olive oil.

On those occasions we obtained fresh fish, any leftovers would be converted into a fish bake. Most certainly wine would not have been included in the original recipe so this is a variation of a favourite dish I recall from childhood.

MPISHI'S FISH BAKE
Serves 6-8

1½ kg white fish (cod, haddock, hake or a combination. Sometimes I include un-dyed smoked cod loin and a few scallops)

350 ml milk / Soya milk + 250 ml dry white wine

1 lemon sliced

1 bay leaf

1 sprig thyme

½ doz black peppercorns

50 gm butter x 2

25 gm 85% flour

2 tbs fresh parsley scissored / chopped

250 gm chestnut mushrooms thinly sliced

Sea salt, ground black pepper and cayenne pepper

1 kg potatoes cooked and mashed with a little hot milk / Soya milk and butter

2 large tomatoes sliced (optional)

50 gm grated Cheddar cheese.

Cook the potatoes, cream with the milk and butter, and keep warm.

Skin the fish. To skin, take firm hold of the tail end of the fish and insert a sharp knife between the skin and the flesh; run the blade away from you and the flesh should separate cleanly from the skin. Or you could ask your fishmonger to do this for you!

Chop the fish into large chunks.

Preheat the oven (Gas 6 / 200 C).

Place the fish in a shallow pan. Add the wine, bay leaf, thyme and peppercorns. Bring to the boil, then lower the heat and poach gently for about 5 minutes until just cooked.

Strain off the liquid. Check for and discard any bones, the lemon slices, bay leaf and peppercorns.

Melt the first 50 gm butter in a saucepan, stir in the flour and cook for 1 min. Add the strained liquid and the milk and bring to the boil, using a balloon whisk until the sauce is smooth and creamy. Remove from the heat. Stir in the parsley and season with salt, pepper and cayenne. Cover with a lid and set to one side.

In a fry pan, heat the remaining butter and sauté the mushrooms for a few minutes until tender. Season and add to the fish.

Combine this mixture with the sauce, stirring carefully and then transfer to an ovenproof casserole dish.

Spread the creamed mashed potato evenly over the fish, fork up the surface and arrange the sliced tomatoes (if using) around the edge.

Sprinkle the top with cheese and bake for 20–25 minutes until browned.

KEDGEREE (VARIATION)
Serves 4

600 gm traditionally smoked un-dyed haddock lightly poached.

1½ cups brown rice cooked (See Section Four)

50 gm butter

1 tbs chopped / scissored parsley

1 or 2 large organic free range eggs

Sea salt and pepper

Traditionally, kedgeree is a mixture of smoked haddock, rice and hard boiled eggs. When my daughter was small she would not tolerate the texture of cooked egg in her mouth so I tried a variation on the original, which she liked!

I serve it as a breakfast or supper dish with warm malted-grain bread rolls.

To poach: place the fish in a shallow fry pan. Cover with cold water and bring to the boil slowly. Simmer for a few minutes. Remove fish with a slotted spoon and keep warm.

Beat the egg(s).

Flake the cooked fish coarsely and combine with the cooked rice.

Melt the butter and stir into the fish mixture with parsley and seasoning. Heat through on the top of the stove in a non-stick pan, stirring. Add the eggs, continuing to stir until well mixed and, when heated through, turn into a pre-heated tureen and serve at once

---

FISH TARTE

Combined with a green salad, this makes an ideal dish for a light lunch.

Line an 8" diameter flan tin with rich short crust pastry made from:

250 gm 85% flour

125 gm butter

¼ tsp salt

Ice-cold water to mix to a soft dough

Sift the flour into a mixing bowl, add the salt and rub in the butter with fingertips to obtain breadcrumb consistency. I rub in a little at a time and I use very cold butter. Then add sufficient cold water to bring the crumbs to a manageable dough. Set aside and chill for ¼ hour before rolling out on a floured surface. Bake blind for 15 minutes in a pre-heated oven (Gas 5 / 190 C).

Filling

200 gm cooked fish flaked. Use a firm fish such as cod, tuna or wild fresh salmon. Smoked un-dyed cod loin is also very good.

4 tomatoes scalded and skinned (optional). If you omit the tomatoes use 250 gm fish.

3 medium onions thinly sliced

25 gm butter

1 dsp flour

75 mg single cream or milk

¼ tsp nutmeg grated

2 organic eggs beaten

50 gm grated hard cheese such as Gruyere or Cheddar

Sea salt and pepper

To bake blind – prick the base of the pastry case with a fork; line it with baking parchment and cover the base with dried beans prior to baking. Remove the beans and baking parchment before adding the filling.

Melt the butter in a fry pan, add the onions and cook until soft. Mix in the flour and stir in the cream / milk. Continue stirring until the sauce thickens and then draw aside and season. Add the beaten eggs and grate in the nutmeg.

Arrange the flaked fish and tomatoes in the bottom of the blind-baked pastry case, season and pour the sauce over the top. Scatter on the grated cheese and bake in the oven for about 30 minutes until golden and set.

Variation:

Cover the bottom of the pastry case with a generous amount of steamed fresh spinach. Place the fish on top. Omit the tomato. Then add a layer of finely chopped cooked leeks. Cover with the sauce, scatter with grated cheese and bake as above.

GRILLED FISH

This is my favourite method for serving fish. It ensures the fish stays succulent, and retains its flavour. It is simple and quick, and allows for extravagance with side dishes and accompaniments. All you need, apart from the fish, is a grill pan and tinfoil, a little butter and lemon juice as an optional extra.

Use thick fish steaks.

Ideal fish for grilling: tuna, swordfish, cod, marlin, salmon, halibut.

Place a generous amount of foil over the grill pan, ensuring it covers the outer sides. Place the fish on top, season and dab with a little butter and squeeze of lemon or lime juice, if using.

Cook under a hot grill for a few minutes, ensuring the fish does not burn. Turn and cook for a further few minutes. 10 minutes in total is sufficient.

Remove from the grill, wrap in the foil and keep warm until required.

Serve with any number of side dishes e.g.

Potato and parsnip cream bake; broad beans with cream; red onion and mushroom tart; roasted red vegetables; rice and cashew nuts; stuffed tomatoes, wild rice, coriander and sweet corn.

**HERRING,
TROUT &
MACKEREL**

Recommended by nutritionists for their omega oil content, they grill well. The fishmonger will gut the fish for you. Remove the head with a sharp knife and split the fish lengthways. Place skin side down on the foil and grill under a medium to hot temperature until cooked.

Trout can be stuffed with a herb-bread / rice, almond and onion mixture. Spoon the stuffing along one side of the split fish. Fold over so that the fish looks whole again and grill on each side.

Mackerel and herring take well to oat flakes: brush the flesh with a little melted butter or oil, dredge in oat flakes, sprinkle with a little lemon juice and grill. They are also delicious fried when coated with fine / pinhead oatmeal.

One school of thought advocates that, in order to maintain harmony within ourselves and the wider world in which we dwell, we consume only what our environment is capable of yielding. In the distant past we may have had no option, particularly in the more remote and inaccessible parts of Britain, where markets would be scarce and itinerant merchants few. This, however, is no longer the case and for most of us, I suspect, such a diet would be too limited and totally at odds with a modern lifestyle that allows for world-wide travel, mass migrations, and a world cuisine brought to us via a TV.

SECTION FOUR
Grains and Pulses

Choice in the 21st century has expanded on all horizons, and if international communication has broadened our eating habits it could also be argued that the cosmopolitan diet allows for more social interaction and international understanding. A curry would faze no-one travelling to the Indian sub-continent: a 2003 survey found that curry was now the favourite national dish. It used to be fish and chips!

The mediaeval Anglo-Saxon diet would have comprised largely barley, oats and rye, a little sheep meat, poultry and poached game and, along the coastal regions, fish. We would have cultivated a vegetable patch and raised onions, leeks, peas, carrots and kale, and cabbages. We would have enjoyed apples, cherries, plums and pears and a lucky few might have tasted an orange, but most certainly we would not have known what to do with a red pepper or whether to cook, peel or plant a banana. We ate nuts and soft berries in season. Wheaten bread, like beef, was the preserve of the rich until the opening up of the Canadian prairie lands, during the latter part of the 19th century, made it available to the common man.

Whatever our origin, our ancestors would marvel at the versatility of the modern British diet: processing, refining, refrigeration and microwaving allow for possibilities unavailable to them. Yet we might keep in mind that our anatomy has not kept pace with sociological and technical advances. That is to say, our dietary requirements differ little from those of our forebears. So whilst enjoying the benefits bestowed by commercial food wizardry, we need to ensure we do not alter the basic substance in such a way as to destroy its potential to nourish us.

Not everyone can tolerate wheat and wheat allergy appears to be on the increase. In some instances gluten, a protein, is the culprit. In others it is the residues of chemicals and pesticides used in commercial crop production. There has even been a suggestion that modern drying and storage methods could be to blame. When the stooks of harvested grain are dried in the open air, the sun releases an enzyme that partially converts the starch into sugars. Seemingly indoor drying does not permit the enzyme release and some people are unable to digest this grain. It could be that we are simply consuming too much wheat, to the exclusion of other grains. Wheat is an excellent food for children inasmuch as it promotes growth. Rye is possibly more suited to the adult since it promotes muscle where refined wheat will encourage the laying down of fat.

The recipes in this section are set out as vegetarian but meat eaters can use many of them as a base and include the meat or fish of their choice. For example, lamb combines well with couscous, fish with rice, chicken with polenta. I have selected grains to highlight my own favourite dishes but the idea is to stimulate imagination and encourage experimentation so the cereal ingredients are interchangeable.

GRAINS

For optimum nutrition grains are consumed as whole grains; if they are ground into meal (a coarser product than flour) or milled, they are utilised for the most part as wholegrain products rather than refined ones. Most people would be familiar with whole wheat as wholewheat bread which is the product of strong wholewheat flour; fewer would be familiar with wheat berries, another term for wheat grains, which can be substituted for brown rice or any other staple.

WHEAT

FRUMENTY is a traditional Northern English breakfast cereal made from soaking wheat berries in cold water for 2–3 hours and then bringing to the boil in 3 times the volume of water, adding a handful of raisins, and leaving to cook overnight in an oven turned to its lowest setting.

There are any number of varieties of wheat which can generally be divided into hard (strong) or soft wheat. British wheat is generally soft whereas American wheat is usually hard because of climate difference. Hard wheat contains more gluten and is better for bread baking, whereas soft wheat is better for pastry and cakes. Maris Dove is the most common British wheat: it is a soft winter wheat with high protein content.

Before cooking wheat berries it is best to dry roast them in a pan for 10 minutes over a medium heat or soak them overnight and use the water as stock. Use 3–4 parts water to berries by volume and allow long, slow cooking for best results.

FRIED WHEAT BERRIES

Chop fine and sauté in ghee or olive oil until soft, a variety of sturdy vegetables such as onions, carrots, parsnips and leeks.

- Add some chopped parsley or watercress, then four cups of cooked wheat berries and stir until the wheat and vegetables are well mixed.
- Add ¼ cup stock or water and 2 tbs tamari or a little Vecon to flavour.
- Season with sea or herb salt, cover and simmer for 5 minutes.

A GUIDE TO COOKING TIMES FOR GRAINS

Times will vary according to how long the grains have been stored.

Barley (Pot/Whole grain)	45 - 60 minutes
Buckwheat	20 minutes
Millet	30 minutes
Oats (groats)	60 minutes
Rolled oats	10 minutes
Polenta (maize meal)	25 minutes
Quinoa	15 minutes
Rice	15–20 minutes
Brown rice	40–60 minutes
Wild rice	60 minutes
Wheat berries	60 minutes

As a rule of thumb use double the amount of water but in those instances where lengthy cooking is required 3–4 times the volume of water is advisable.

RICE

Rice used to be synonymous with milk puddings and enjoyed little popularity until the introduction and spread of Indian and Chinese Cuisine, and Takeaways. Traditionally the staple crop of the East, rice is nowadays recognised by nutritionists world-wide as an invaluable food and, alongside oats, is probably our most widely consumed cereal after wheat.

COOKING RICE

WHITE, LONG GRAIN / BASMATI RICE

I usually steam this type of rice for best results. I use ¼ cup rice to 100 ml lightly salted water per person and steam in an electric steamer for 20 minutes.

Another method is to allow 1cup rice to 1½ cups water. Bring to the boil, add a pinch of sea salt, and immediately turn down the heat to its lowest setting. Cover with a tight fitting lid. About 20 minutes later all the water will be absorbed and the grains tender and ready to eat.

My father was adept with rice, having produced many curries over his entire adult life. He would use the above quantities for 4 servings, bring to the boil and continue to boil rapidly for five minutes. Then he would turn off the heat, cover with a tight fitting lid and the rice would be ready in 15 minutes.

WHOLEGRAIN RICE requires 2 cups water to 1 cup rice and will take 40 minutes rather than 20 minutes for the rice to cook through.

Nutritional Tip:
A little butter stirred into the rice just prior to serving will impart a lovely flavour and enrich it.

WILD RICE is unrelated to other types of rice, being of a different species altogether. Nutritionally it is superior: it contains twice the protein of refined white rice, 6 times the amount of B1 (thiamine) and B3, 6 times the amount of iron and 20 times more B2 (riboflavin). It is more expensive than rice.

UNPROCESSED (BROWN) RICE is nutritionally richer than refined rice. Despite this my family prefers white to brown rice so I tend to compromise, using white rice as an accompaniment, and brown when it is the staple ingredient of a recipe. The exception to this is my Rice Salad (Section 1– August) which definitely tastes better for being made with white Basmati rice.

Rice Water is an excellent remedy for weak stomachs, upset stomachs or diarrhoea. Because I do not favour prescriptive remedies I recommend it at the first hint of trouble. It can be safely given to infants by the teaspoonful to prevent dehydration and to get valuable B vitamins back into to the gut.

Wash a handful of organic wholegrain (brown) rice and put in a pan with a litre of water. Add ½ teaspoon sea salt. Bring to the boil. Turn down the heat and cover with a well fitting lid. Simmer for 1 hour. Strain the liquid and administer warm in small quantities, a teaspoon to a tablespoonful at a time as required (every 10 minutes or every ½ hour depending on the severity of the symptoms).

Bach's Rescue Remedy can be safely added to the rice water if symptoms are extreme. Use the dosage as recommended on the bottle.

NUT RISOTTO
Serves 4

2 tbs ghee or 4 tbs olive oil

1 large onion finely chopped

2 cloves garlic finely chopped

225 gm or generous 1 cup Arborio (Italian) rice

105 ml dry white wine

1½ litres vegetable stock, or water plus 1 dsp vegetable stock powder

125 gm chestnut mushrooms quartered

Generous handful (more or less according to taste) salted roasted cashew nuts.

Tomato purée (optional)

1 tbs finely chopped parsley

Sea salt and freshly ground black pepper

Heat the ghee / oil in a heavy-based pan and fry the onion and garlic until soft.

Add the rice and stir until all the grains are well coated with oil / ghee. Pour on the wine and stir over a medium heat until it has been absorbed.

Ladle in 150 ml stock and cook, stirring constantly, until the rice has absorbed all the liquid. Continue stirring and adding stock in similar amounts until half is left. Stir in the mushrooms and cook for 2–3 minutes.

Add the remaining liquid as before, until the rice is cooked. It should be creamy and the grains tender. Stir in the lemon juice and parsley, and purée if using. Stir in the cashew nuts and warm through. Season and serve at once on pre-warmed plates.

Accompany with crusty bread and mixed salad / baby broad beans and cream; minted fresh peas.

Variations:
• Use toasted flaked almonds in place of cashew nuts.
• Use broad beans and / or peas in place of nuts.
• Use shellfish such as king prawns, mussels, chunks of cod loin, scallops instead of nuts.
• Use chopped, cooked leftover chicken breast in place of nuts. Add a few pinenuts.
• Include some chopped red, green and orange peppers.

STUFFED RED PEPPERS / TOMATOES
Serves 4

4 red peppers or beefsteak tomatoes

50 gm cooked sweet corn kernels

100 gm cooked wild rice (50 gm if using tomatoes)

1 clove garlic

50 gm grated mature organic Cheddar cheese

Sea salt and pepper

A little olive oil

1 tbs chopped fresh coriander

2 tbs vegetable stock if using tomatoes instead of peppers

Cut the tops off the peppers and remove the seeds and white ridges. Retain the tops. Mix all the remaining ingredients together, except the oil, and season to taste. Spoon the mixture into the peppers, piling it higher in the centre. Sprinkle the oil over the top, arrange the peppers in an ovenproof dish, replace the tops, and bake in a pre-heated oven (Gas 4 180 C) for about 20 minutes until cooked through.

If using tomatoes instead of peppers, after cutting off the tops, remove the seeds. Scoop out the flesh and chop finely, including the cut tops. Simmer these in a pan with a close fitting lid until tender. Drain. Proceed as for the Red Peppers using 50 gm rice plus the cooked tomato Tops are omitted from the tomato version. Instead, just prior to serving, place a parsley floret in the centre of each tomato.

Variations:

• Use wholewheat breadcrumbs in place of rice

• Mushrooms in place of sweet corn

• Include a little onion, sage and parsley (in place of the coriander)

• Replace the corn with pine nuts

• Add some raisins. Use Gruyere or Jarlsberg cheese in place of mature Cheddar and halve the quantity.

OATS

Oats in this country are traditionally associated with the Scots and, thanks to clever advertising by one particular manufacturer, with strength and resilience. It is true – oats are a warming, nourishing cereal with the ability to sustain man and beast over long periods. They provide energy, some protein, essential roughage in the form of fibre and many of the B group vitamins essential for a healthy nervous system.

There is a tradition on the west coast of Scotland that porridge is good for the eyes. We now know that inositol, one of the complex B vitamins, is found in high concentration in the eye lens. Oats are rich in inositol and harbour more thiamin (B1) than any other breakfast cereal. They also contain a gummy fibre to which excess cholesterol attaches itself in order to be safely eliminated through the digestive tract. So the humble oat has much to recommend itself.

Recipes for oats can be found in Sections 1, 2 and 6

MILLET

Millet, disparaged as "budgie-food", is particularly rich in iron and makes a palatable substitute for rice in savoury dishes. Ground into a "meal" it can be used as a nourishing porridge for infants. This is also a good substitute for wheat flour as a thickener for gravies and is particularly flavoursome when made into a sauce for lasagne.

This is the only alkaline grain which makes it readily digestible and an excellent food for those trying to reduce their acid intake. It is rich in silicon, the substance that helps build collagen for keeping skin, eyes, nails and arteries healthy.

Cooked, the yellow grain turns fluffy and white. After rinsing, dry roast the millet in a pan to remove the water and sauté in a little sunflower oil to bring out the flavour. Add the water, bring to the boil and simmer.

An alternative cooking method for millet is to bring four cups of water to the boil and then stir in 1 cup millet with a pinch of salt. Lower the heat and cover with a tight-fitting lid. It will take around 15–25 minutes for the grain to absorb the water.

The grain combines well with root vegetables and onions to make a vegetable stew. Add a little tamari or vecon for enhanced flavour.

I often substitute millet for rice. It is delicious with a vegetable curry or any Middle Eastern spiced dish.

MILLET CROQUETTES

200 gm millet

150 gm hard mature cheese grated

1 onion finely chopped

50 gm mushrooms finely sliced

1–2 tbs freshly chopped parsley

Sea salt and black pepper

1 tbs ghee

Sunflower oil for shallow frying

1 organic egg beaten with a little milk or Soya milk

Fresh wholemeal breadcrumbs / wheatgerm / oatgerm to coat

Cook the millet. Heat the ghee in a fry pan and cook the onion and mushroom until tender.

In a bowl combine the millet and onion / mushroom mixture and stir in the cheese. Season. With lightly-floured hands shape the mixture into small croquettes, dip into the beaten egg and milk and then roll in the breadcrumbs. Fry in hot oil until golden on all sides. Drain on kitchen paper and serve hot.

MILLET SOUFFLE

125 gm cooked millet

3 organic eggs yolks, beaten

½ pint milk or Soya milk

50 gm grated mature Cheddar cheese or mild cheese plus ½ tsp mustard

3 egg whites stiffly beaten

Sea salt and pepper

A little extra grated cheese for sprinkling on top

Combine all the ingredients, folding in the stiffly beaten egg whites last (use a metal spoon). Pour into a greased baking dish and top with a little extra grated cheese. Place the dish in a roasting pan $^2/_3{}^{rd}$ filled with hot water and bake in a moderate oven (Gas 4 180 C) until set, 20–30 minutes.

BARLEY

Barley is nowadays used mostly in the brewing trade or as a fattener for pigs. In times when fragmentary dietary habits and environmental pollution places more and more strain upon our kidneys, we might consider re-incorporating barley into the human diet as this grain has long been recognised as having a soothing and strengthening affect on these organs. Like millet, it can be substituted for wheat as a thickener and for sauces.

LEMON BARLEY WATER

A kidney tonic and remedy for acute cystitis.

Take one large man-sized handful pot barley, wash and bring to the boil in 600 ml fresh cold water. Turn off the heat and strain, discarding the liquid.

Rinse the pan, replace the barley and add 1 litre fresh cold water plus the washed pared rind of either an organic or scrubbed un-waxed lemon. Bring to the boil, turn down the heat, cover with a well-fitting lid and simmer for 20 minutes or until the barley is soft. Strain off the liquid, sweeten with a little honey or, if a more savoury flavour is favoured, a little sea salt.

Drink the resulting barley milk warm in small quantities.

For cystitis: drink as much as you can every 10 minutes. I used to suffer intermittently from this painful complaint and would clear it within 24 hours using this remedy. The barley mash can be re-boiled using a fresh litre of water with a fresh lemon paring.

BARLEY PUDDING   Barley pudding is excellent for growing children and for convalescing invalids.

I sometimes use barley flakes as an alternative to pudding rice for a milk pudding, using either whole milk or Soya milk, a walnut sized piece of butter and natural cane sugar to taste. It takes about an hour for the barley to absorb the milk when cooked in a moderate oven (Gas 4 180 C). If you prefer a less solid milk pudding reduce the cooking time.

Variations

- Adding a beaten egg will enrich the dish
- Grate a little nutmeg over the top prior to placing in the oven to add an interesting flavour
- Add 1 tbs raisins

MAIZE
Sweet Corn
/ Polenta

Maize is a very versatile cereal and a staple food in many African countries. I have vivid childhood memories of my ayah with her female relatives and friends pounding dried maize kernels into a meal which was later cooked as posho, a kind of porridge, served with a stew of vegetables, meat or fish.

The receptacle used was an inverted, hollowed-out wooden cone with a solid standing base. Maize was poured into the receptacle and two women would take up a position opposite each other in a beautifully aligned stance, bare feet firmly placed on the ground about hip-width apart. Then, both armed with a sturdy pole, they would alternately pound the kernels into a mash of fine meal. This was a rhythmic task often accompanied by singing to keep them going. I recall the Africans often sang not only when engaged in heavy work such as this, or when manually pulling a ferry across a river, but whenever they were working communally at a seemingly mundane task.

Other occasions that come to mind are of circles of women squatting or sitting crossed-legged on the ground with shallow baskets in their laps sifting the chaff from rice or maize and, with a deft flick of the fingers, tossing away the offending material. A good deal of laughter, interspersed with chatter and gossip, accompanied the process while one eye was always on the children playing in the background. There was no overseer suggesting they would be more productive by working in silence and attending solely to the task in hand. Socialising was integral to the labour, and undoubtedly lightened the workload.

It may be naïve but my abiding child memory of these women was that they were for the most part happy. This was also my adult impression some forty years later when, on a visit to India, I found women similarly engaged in simple hands-on communal work, sorting rice. There was radiance in their visage that bespoke a connection not only with their companions but with their production. In other words they were wholly engaged with what was occupying them. This is Meditation.

It occurred to me on my return from New Zealand that our modern lifestyle mostly precludes the habit of "calling in" on friends without prior arrangement. And it is a long time since I have heard children singing spontaneously.

In my yoga classes mantra or chanting is consistently the least popular suggestion on the agenda, mainly because of self-consciousness or conviction in an inability to sing. This is a pity because there is nothing like singing to bond and lift the human spirit. Go to any voice workshop organised by someone like Jill Purce (in London and Devon) and notice the difference in the feeling of wellbeing generated: it can last for weeks!

I once had the opportunity of taking the actress and voice therapist, Harriet Buchan, into HMP Acklington to give a workshop for my yoga students. It had an immediate uplifting effect on their spirits and they were still talking about it months later. One young man, having been told in boyhood that he was tone deaf, suddenly discovered he had a rich baritone voice after all. There was no silencing him after that! Singing, like poetry, is the voice of the spirit that needs feeding and expression as much as body and mind.

SUNSHINE SLICE
Serves 8

1½ cups Soya milk, whole organic cow's milk or goat's milk

1 cup polenta

½ cup plain flour

2 large organic eggs beaten

2 sweet corn cooked and de-husked.

4–6 tbs grated Parmesan cheese

1 tsp baking powder

Sea salt

Generous amount olive oil to cover the base of a large non-stick fry pan

Steam the sweet corn and when cool enough to handle remove the kernels with a sharp knife. Set aside in a basin.

In a large mixing bowl stir the polenta with the flour. Add the beaten eggs, and then gradually beat in the Soya milk or whole milk to obtain a batter. Season with a little sea salt. Add the sweet corn and Parmesan cheese and mix well prior to chilling for ½ an hour in the fridge.

When ready to serve heat the oil in the fry pan.

Stir 1 tsp baking powder into the corn batter and then pour into the fry pan. Using a spatula keep pushing the "pancake" towards the centre from the edge of the pan until most of the batter has been incorporated and cooked in the oil. Then take a plate large enough to cover the pan, invert the pan so that the pancake drops onto the plate, and then carefully slide it back into the fry pan to cook the underside for a few more minutes. It should be crispy golden.

Using a spatula, turn the cooked pancake onto a pre-heated plate and serve immediately, dividing it into 8 portions with a sharp knife.

Accompany with a purée of carrots, white turnips, parsnips and butternut; and a large mixed green salad. The colours combine wonderfully and the different textures tantalise the most jaded palette.

This was a great success one wet March day with some of my yoga students who, for want of a name, called it Sunshine Slice.

CORN CROQUETTES
Serves 4

3 tbs butter

3 tbs flour

300 ml Soya or whole milk

Sea salt and freshly ground black pepper

2 tbs chopped parsley

2½ cups sweet corn kernels cooked

2 organic egg yolks

Coating

2 organic eggs beaten or 1 whole egg beaten with a little Soya or whole milk

Seasoned flour

Wholewheat breadcrumbs

Olive oil for shallow frying

Melt the butter in a heavy-based pan, stir in the flour and cook for a few minutes until pale gold. Remove from the heat and gradually add the milk, stirring all the time until thoroughly blended. Return to the heat and stir until thickened. Season with sea salt and pepper.

Turn off the heat, stir in the cooked corn, egg yolks and parsley. Chill for 1 hour. The mixture should have a heavy consistency that allows for shaping into croquettes between floured hands.

Dip each croquette into the beaten egg or egg and milk mixture, roll in flour and breadcrumbs and fry in hot olive oil until crisp. Drain on kitchen paper and serve immediately on a pre-heated dish.

Accompany with green beans, Brussels sprouts, peas and a purée of root vegetables.

PULSES   Peas, beans and lentils, (and peanuts!) are legumes that are often served as vegetables, or used in soups; combined with grains in vegetarian recipes they ensure a complete protein intake. Peanuts, of course, are a favourite snack-food. What is probably less well known is that pea flour was often combined with grain flours in the Middle-Ages to make bread.

PEAS   Pease pudding is a well-known accompaniment to ham in Northeast England, and Pease brose used to be an alternative to oat porridge as a breakfast dish in Scotland. The latter is now very difficult to obtain, possibly because breakfast is so much out of favour with the young or it could be due to the proliferation and popularity of commercially packaged cereals. This is a pity because it is absolutely delicious. Savoury in flavour, smooth textured and of the consistency of thick custard, it is traditionally eaten piping hot and accompanied with a bowlful of cold milk. It is also an exceedingly nutritious food and an ideal way to begin the new day when blood sugar levels are low.

PEASE PUDDING

200 gm yellow split peas rinsed

A large square of muslin or a pudding cloth

This traditional Tyneside accompaniment to boiled ham is favoured particularly at New Year. Split peas are the main ingredient. These are dried peas without the skins and they cook more quickly than most legumes.

Place the peas in the centre of the cloth, pick up the 4 corners and tie in a knot, leaving room for the peas to expand during cooking. Tie a piece of string around the knot.

Place the pudding cloth in a pan of boiling water containing a ham joint / hock simmering in a variety of root vegetables and onions. Ensure that the other end of the string is tied to the base of the pan handle for easy removal when the pudding is cooked. Simmer for 1 hour or longer.

Remove the pudding from the ham broth, squeeze out the excess liquid and untie the cloth to retrieve the pudding ball. Serve separately, either hot or cold, sliced. It will have taken up the ham and vegetable flavour.

Pease pudding sandwiches used to be as common as chip butties are today.

This pudding is delicious served cold with cold boiled ham and salad and buttered minted new potatoes.

For a vegetarian alternative, prepare the peas in a cloth as above and boil in a pan of salted water until cooked (approximately 1 hour). Remove the cloth and turn the peas into a large mixing bowl. Combine with 1 large onion, very finely chopped and softened in hot oil or butter. Add a good knob of butter, season with sea salt and black pepper and mash thoroughly. The mixture should be quite stiff. Turn into a dish or mould and serve hot or cold in slices.

LENTILS

Lentils allegedly formed the "mess of pottage" given to Esau by Jacob. They are a highly nutritious and versatile food of two main types: Chinese and Indian. The former vary from whitish to green while the latter come in various shades of pink to red. Red lentils contain more protein than the others.

Cooked whole lentils make an excellent substitute for mince. This can be useful where the company is a mix of vegetarian and meat eaters. Wash the lentils thoroughly and cook in plenty of salted water or vegetable stock until tender. This usually takes about 30 minutes.

Drain and use as you would minced beef or lamb. Retain the cooking water / stock for "gravy". I combine them with onion, garlic, chopped tomatoes and herbs as a base for a cottage pie / moussaka. They combine well with other pulses such as peas / broad beans and make excellent curry, accompanied by rice / millet / quinoa / couscous.

LENTIL BAKE
Serves 4

250 gm puy or brown lentils washed and soaked in boiling water for 1 hour.

60 ml sunflower or olive oil

1 large onion finely diced

1 clove garlic crushed

150 gm sliced button mushrooms.

300 ml vegetable stock

Sea salt and ground black pepper

1 dsp fresh chopped herbs / 1 tsp dried mixed herbs

¼ tsp paprika

1 organic egg beaten

60 ml cream or Soya cream

Two large skinned and thickly sliced tomatoes

1 tbs fresh chopped parley or coriander leaf for garnish

Drain the lentils and add to the stock in a deep saucepan. Bring to the boil, turn down the heat, cover with a tight-fitting lid and simmer until softened – about 30–40 minutes. Leave to stand until most of the liquid has been absorbed.

Heat the oil in a casserole or deep fry pan and cook the onions and garlic until translucent. Add the mushrooms and cook, stirring, until softened.

Mix the lentils with the cooked vegetables, beaten egg, herbs and cream. Season well and turn into a greased loaf tin, smoothing the surface. Arrange the tomatoes on top and bake in a moderate oven (Gas 4 180 C) for ½ an hour.

Garnish with the parsley or coriander and serve with a selection of fresh seasonal vegetables.

LENTIL BAKE 2
Serves 6-8

250 gm split red lentils washed

125 gm wholewheat breadcrumbs

1 tbs ghee or 2 tbs sunflower or olive oil

1 large onion sliced

1 clove garlic crushed

125 gm finely sliced chestnut mushrooms

1 tin organic chopped tomatoes strained; retain the liquid

1 tbs tomato puree

1 tsp mixed dried herbs

200 ml vegetable stock

¼ tsp ground cumin, sea salt and freshly ground black pepper

Squeeze of fresh lemon juice

1large organic beaten egg (optional)

Some fresh chopped parsley for garnish

Cook the lentils in the vegetable stock until tender. Drain, retaining the liquid. Mix this with the drained tomato juice.

Sauté the onion mushrooms and garlic in the ghee / oil until softened.

In a large mixing bowl combine the lentils with all the ingredients, except the tomato and lentil liquids and the egg. Mix thoroughly with a wooden spoon. The resulting consistency should be that of a soft dough; if it is too dry / crumbly add carefully some of the retained tomato and lentil liquid.

For a firmer bake or if the bake is to be sliced cold add the beaten egg and mix thoroughly.

Turn into a greased loaf tin and bake in a moderate oven for approximately 30 minutes (Gas 4 180 C).

Garnish with parsley prior to serving and accompany with fresh seasonal vegetables.

This lentil bake is good eaten cold and can be used for picnics.

Variation
Add 1 level tsp mild or medium curry powder in place of the cumin.

THE STORE CUPBOARD

DRY STORES

Grains, pulses and nuts keep well provided they are stored correctly: in airtight, dry containers in clean cupboards, situated ideally in the coolest part of the kitchen.

Whole grains and pulses will keep for 9–12 months

Ground grain – wholemeal flours and flaked grains should be consumed within 6 months.

Nuts should be consumed within 12 weeks unless bought in their shells when they will keep for 6 months or more.

OILS

Unless you use large quantities, oils should be bought in small amounts, be cold-pressed and kept out of direct sunlight. I transfer litres of olive oil into brown glass bottles.

Keep transparent bottles wrapped in a thick covering of brown paper.

Once heated, any residual oil should be discarded.

CONDIMENTS

Salt and whole black peppercorns will keep indefinitely.

Discard dried herbs after 6 months.

Spices will keep slightly longer but their food value decreases over time.

Purées should be kept in a refrigerator once opened and consumed according to manufacturers' instructions. For single people they are best bought in the smallest quantity – usually in glass jars – and used up quickly. If no refrigerator is available

ensure the top is replaced firmly, store in the coolest part of the kitchen and use within 3 days.

Jams store well because of their sugar content. Sugar-free spreads need to be stored according to manufacturers' instructions.

Honey will keep indefinitely. Runny honey may solidify, especially in cold weather.

Bottled sauces such as tamari Soya sauce: read the "best before" date.

DAIRY

Best stored in a refrigerator or bought daily. Hard cheese which is salt-laden will keep out of the refrigerator provided it is well wrapped and stored in a cool airy position.

Store eggs in a cool airy place rather than in the 'fridge.

VEGETABLES

See Section Five.

THE SECRET OF SUCCESSFUL STORING

Buy food as fresh as possible, store in clean dry airy surrounds, and consume as soon as possible.

Buy economically – if you live alone or as a couple, most independent wholefood shops will oblige you with smaller quantities than chain stores. If you have a large family, bulk buying makes sense. During the '70s, whilst living in Gisborne, NZ, a group of young mothers met together and organised a small co-operative whereby both fresh and dry produce was delivered weekly to our street. Each house took turn as the distribution point, where we all gathered to make up the orders, socialise and generally have a good laugh, whilst the children were safely occupied under one roof or out in the garden. It certainly took the tedium out of shopping.

STOCKING THE CUPBOARD

PULSES   A selection of the following:–

Aduki beans – good for casseroles

Alfalfa seeds – good for sprouting, buy by the 25 gm

Brown lentils – go well with grains

Flageolet – a delicate flavoured bean, delicious in salads; expensive

Green lentils – make delicious sprouts, combine well with rice

Kidney beans – red and black – stews and casseroles

Pintos, rosecocos, blackeyes, butter beans, cannelini – good in casseroles

Soup mix – useful for singles wanting a selection of beans in small quantity

Split peas – soups

Split (red) lentils – excellent for soups, the quickest cooking lentils

GRAINS	**Rice** – long and short grain organic brown rice; white basmati for special occasions; arborio for risotto
	Wheat – good for sprouting, and for casseroles; buy in very small quantities unless using regularly
	Millet – excellent substitute for rice; the flour makes good sauces; contains the highest iron content of all the cereals
	Bulghur wheat – this is pre-cooked and should not be kept beyond 3 months
	Oats – "meal" or rolled
	Couscous – delicious alternative to rice
	Barley – pot or whole, pearled for soups; flaked for desserts or muesli
	Rye – as flour or flakes for muesli

FLOURS	**For bread** – whole wheat, granary, unbleached strong white
	General purpose: 85% / 81% wheat meal flour; chuppatty; unbleached plain or SR white
	Semolina – winter desserts
	Soya – high protein content enriches bread; sauces
	Rice – winter desserts, infant porridge and convalescence

PASTA	All varieties store well for at least 6 months – check "best before" date

DRIED FRUITS	Currants, raisins, sultanas – for general baking and snacks
	Apricots, peaches, dates, figs, prunes, apple rings (wash well prior to use to remove sulphur preservative)

SPREADS

Nut butters	Marmalade
Sugar-free spreads	Lemon curd
Honey	Jams
Butter	Pâtés

FLAVOURINGS

Sea salt	Vegetable / tomato purée
Black pepper	Miso for casseroles and flavouring
Selection of herbs and spices	Selection of dried sea vegetables for casseroles
Vegetable stock cubes or powder	

MISCELLANEOUS

Nuts	Sweet pickle for sandwiches
Beverages	Molasses
Soya milk	Maple and rice syrups
Biscuits – rye, oat cakes, rice cakes etc.	Barley malt
Demerara sugar, natural cane sugar, natural cane caster sugar	
Sugar-free organic baked beans for convenience	
Organic chopped tinned tomatoes.	
Cider vinegar, raspberry, balsamic and wine vinegars	

SECTION FIVE
Vegetables– Cooked or Raw?

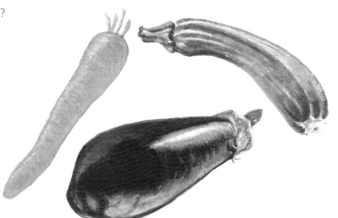

INTRODUCTION

Of all the life forms on Planet Earth only humans cook their food. According to the nutritional philosopher, Rudolph Hauschka it requires an innate understanding of plants and their rhythmic cycles to know whether they should be eaten cooked or raw.

Hauschka was a follower of Rudolph Steiner, the anthroposophist (spiritual scientist), whose teachings underpin the rationale behind biodynamic cultivation. Anthroposophy requires that we look beyond the immediately apparent, or the merely physical attributes of Life, to see what is meant in order to understand the Kingdom of Nature. Biodynamics is art and science.

Modern physics allows that all matter is simply consciousness in dense arrested form or as David Bohm succinctly stated, "All matter is frozen light" (energy). So matter – mineral, vegetable and animal – is a combination of fact and description, a condensed picture demonstrating the soul or life force.

PLANTS

Anthroposophy describes plants as light beings rooted to the earth and under the direct control of cosmic forces. They span the space between earth and sky. The polarities between darkness and light are constantly relating to both. That is to say: plants' roots are pulled by the earth's gravitational forces into the darkness while their leaves and blossoms reach upwards towards the light.

Compare a carrot (a root) with broccoli (stem and flower) or a strawberry (a fruit): the densities and textures are altogether different. At one end of the scale we have matter – subject to Earth forces – manifesting in dense compacted form; at the other, the material – governed by celestial forces – is comparatively ephemeral.

Starch (carbohydrate) is plant material formed from cosmic forces as well as light, air and water. These cosmic, warm, expansive, ripening forces refine this starch material into blossom substance which is then sublimated into sugar and ripened fruit.

The plant's green centre is the starting point and the sublimation process moves from there upwards. It could be said that the green centre is the heart of the plant. In the other direction, cold, contracting, gravitational earth forces lay hold on the starch to give solidity and structure: the further down the plant we travel the firmer and woodier we find it. Cellulose is also carbohydrate but a more compact substance than the starches and sugars.

Correspondingly, the human heart-chakra is depicted as green and is the mid-point between the three so-called higher chakras and the three lower ones. Chakras belong to our energetic system and act both independently and interdependently as energy transformers. They cannot be seen by the naked eye any more than we can see electricity but in both cases we are able to measure the effects! For a comprehensive and readily understood treatise on this subject get hold of a copy of *"Everything You've Always Wanted to Know About Your Body (but so far no-one's been able to tell you)"* by Chris Thomas and Diane Baker.

Life requires warmth to unfold and heat raises energy. We burn up food during digestion and metabolism; or, more specifically – by breaking the chemical bonds between carbon atoms and carbon and hydrogen atoms, we absorb the heat released by this breakdown process. Human warmth allows the vital processes to flow smoothly. This apart, on an intrinsic level we talk about warm-hearted individuals and we gravitate towards them because we feel nurtured in their company. They uplift our mood and enhance our spirits. We digest their warmth and radiate it back.

"Warmth, moisture, darkness and time are the elements of cooking and they are also the elements of digestion." (Colbin) So cooking could be described as a measure of pre-digestion inasmuch as it takes over some of the work done by the stomach, pancreas and liver and renders the food easier for the body to absorb the nutrients it requires. It has been suggested that the introduction of cooking may have been the decisive factor in leading us away from a primarily animal existence into a more fully human one. Only humans think intellectually, write and speak. Colbin further suggests that the application of fire to food may have resulted in the development of civilisation by allowing for mental focus and concentration.[1]

Our digestive system is intricately linked with our emotional and nervous systems and the link is symbiotic: when we are unhappy we either cannot eat or we binge. We can get mental blocks from physical constipation. When a lot of energy is spent on digestion our capacity for thinking is correspondingly diminished. Writing a dissertation or engaging in a strenuous yoga workout after a heavy meal becomes an effort; we are better for taking a short nap or going for a brisk walk to awaken our sleepy senses.

Food faddism has become a fetish in the West: there are always "new" discoveries, variations to the modern diet that border on contortions. The food industry is mirroring the fashion industry: what is this week or month's flavour or special diet? We have the vitamin brigade, the low-fat, high protein, calorie-counting, high fibre and raw food brigades – to name a few. None of these is rational in the holistic kitchen where relationship and inter-connections are more valid than the separate components of a vegetable or a lamb chop.

If cooking equates with imitating Nature – that is to say intuitively as well as intellectually – and we attend to it correctly, then we will enhance the quality of our diet. This entails different methods of cooking depending on whether the raw material derives from the blossom, root or leafy part of the plant.

The blossom is the area to which spiritual forces devote most of the ripening, liberating warmth forces. To go beyond this is to invite decay. Cooking the upper portions of a plant carries them beyond the stage desirable in Nature, which is analogous with dying. Food scientists would talk about the vitamin content being destroyed. So when brewing blossom teas such as linden blossom, it is better to scald and allow an infusion to take place rather than boiling. And take them fresh: soft berry fruits such as strawberries or raspberries instinctively taste better when freshly picked. If these are cooked it is usually to make jam. The taste, texture and colour are altogether different and it requires the addition of sugar, in quantity, to support and sustain the otherwise collapsed cooked fruit. Granted there are recipes for cooked oranges but most people would equate cooking citrus with marmalade.

Root vegetables belong to the opposite polarity. The earth has shielded them from the ripening sun forces, so cooking gives carrots, beets and parsnips what they failed to obtain in outer Nature. Cooking lifts them into the higher dimension of cosmic warmth activity. They are lifted above the ground and sweetened by the cooking process. By and large a cooked carrot will taste sweeter than a raw one. Thus they are the more easily digested by us.

Leaves belong in the centre or middle zone. They are more blossom-like the higher up the plant they grow. Brief cooking lifts leaves up to the blossom stage, where over-cooking (cabbage "done to death") will take it too far and we are left with collapsed material. The life-force will have disappeared into the cooking water or, as the food scientists would say, the vitamin content will have been lost. 5–10 minutes is adequate for leafy greens.

Some leafy vegetables object to being cooked at all. We do not as a rule eat boiled lettuce. Consider the delicacy of a lettuce leaf: it is almost transparent. It is gentle, warm, feminine.

Apples are crisp and juicy in the summer and are best eaten raw but, stored beyond December, they take on something of the root quality of the plant and baked apple dishes are very appealing during the winter months. Eating strawberry or raspberry jam in winter serves as a reminder of a bygone summer not only through flavour but scent as well. It summons up a sense of warmth to encourage sustenance through the colder seasons. Put another way, it lifts the spirits to sustain us physically during the long dark days, rousing us to action when we would prefer to remain curled up under a warm duvet!

Through the medium of cooking we are involved in that alchemy in which our entire cosmos is engaged. This serves to remind us not only of how infinitesimal we are but, awesomely, how significant we are within that grand design or cosmic plan that is constantly unfolding. The whole yoga philosophy emphasises at-one-ment with our self and all creation. Our entire relationship with food allows us to experience and realise this one basic Truth as forcefully as any other form of meditation. Undoubtedly some of our ancestors were well practiced in the connection without ever having heard the word yoga.

Steaming, boiling, roasting, and braising are all methods suited to cooking vegetables. One of my favourites is sweating them in a little olive oil and then placing a well-fitting lid over the pan and letting them cook in their own juices. They are thereby enriched and vegetarians, in particular, are less likely to experience a feeling of chilliness if they take up some of their vegetable matter in this way.

A raw food diet can actually strain the organism. As part of an experiment I once undertook a totally raw food regime for 1 summer month, in New Zealand. By the end of it I felt quite ill: I found the diet physically unsatisfying; I was mentally unfocused and somewhat disorientated. Those who had advocated this "healthy regime" were quite disappointed when I said I would not recommend it but digestion is not meant to be a labour of Hercules. An occasional challenge, however, such as a juice or raw food fast is healthy, strengthening and stimulating. I like to partake of such a fast towards the beginning of spring just to throw off the heavy sluggish feelings of winter.

Raw food advocates voice concern about vitamin loss through cooking but this view accounts only for the outer forms, not the nature of vitamins. Considering how so much food is processed in the West there is some reason for alarm but a diet consisting entirely, or even mostly, of raw foods makes as little sense as supplementing with artificial vitamins. If we cook with a mind towards transforming instead of destroying our food (overcooking it) then we will be enhancing our diet with cooked matter, and we supplement with appropriate raw material such as a piece of fruit.

Experience has led me to conclude that a raw food diet, carried to extremes, overtaxes the organism so that neither body nor spirit is properly supported – not to mention the metabolic problems that can arise. Cows eat raw grass and then chew the cud. They have an extra stomach designed specifically for this purpose. We do not!

In the final analysis, I believe a balanced diet comprises both cooked and raw foods; and how much of one in relation to the other will be determined by many considerations, not least of which will be personal preferences. Seasonal factors also play a part. Raw foods (cool, fresh, juicy foods) are probably more appealing in summer than in winter when hot, substantial broths, stews and fruit crumbles provide as much a psychological as a physical barrier against the freezing cold. Seasonal considerations apart, I tend to regard raw foods mostly as therapy (e.g. fasting) and cooked ones as nourishment. Traditional Chinese medicine suggests eating too much raw food results in energies, which should be serving higher mental and spiritual functions, being called upon to help with digestion.

[1] Anne-Marie Colbin *"Food and Healing"* pp 196-7

BASIC GUIDELINES

Vegetables are an excellent source of minerals, vitamins and enzymes which are essential to health. They can be served up in endless varieties as salads, soups or meals in their own right. Ideally a small portion of raw vegetable or fruit is consumed daily to counterbalance the cooked food. Vegetables are also a rich source of fibre which is essential for comfortable evacuation of waste matter.

Buy produce as fresh as possible from a source as close to where they were grown. Organic green beans look tempting in our supermarkets but if they come from Zambia or Egypt, they will be the product of a different energy field than our own. This is not necessarily "bad" in any real sense, but we are part of the landscape in which we live and on an energetic level will harmonise better with foods produced closer to home. And if that is not a consideration then maybe the ethical and ecological concerns are. Third World countries are being encouraged to produce crops for us on land that might be better suited to produce for the home market. And it takes an enormous amount of fuel to airlift these crops on a daily basis to our supermarkets.

A lot of supermarket vegetables are neatly trimmed and plastic wrapped. Vegetables sold with their leaves intact and with soil still clinging to their roots retain moisture and freshness longer. Trimming vegetables reduces their life expectancy. Local farmers' markets are becoming increasingly popular and are a viable alternative to the supermarket. Using these will encourage farmers to produce what we want. And, more importantly, what we need.

Use organic produce where available: all genuine organic produce carries the symbol of the Soil Association or the European equivalent on produce from abroad.

- The vitamin C content of fruit and vegetables is highest at the point of picking but, if shopping only once or twice weekly, eat on the day of purchase those vegetables to which freshness is most important.

- Lettuce is only valuable fresh.

- Store in the least cold part of a fridge or a north-facing larder.

- Protect roots and leeks, which may have been blanched during growing, from the light.

- Avoid bruising by not packing too close together.

- Frozen vegetables are not an ideal source of food. "In Nature Form is as important as Content in respect of Function." (Anne-Marie Colbin op.cit. p 46). When a pea is frozen the water content in it expands and its outer wall collapses, which is why the packaging suggests you tip the frozen product directly into boiling water – leaving them to thaw out will produce evidence of a collapsed pea. All the bits may still be present but they will not be operating in the same way as a robust fresh pea. Energetically we cannot interact with a dead, frozen pea in the same way as we can with a live, fresh one. Both types (fresh and frozen) will feed the physical organism. That is to say we can feel physically satisfied with a dish of cooked frozen peas but on an intrinsic level biodynamics would state that we are not nourished. Mentally and spiritually we are better nourished by fresh produce because the energy field is intact.

Shape (form) influences us intimately at a very deep, albeit unconscious, level. The next time you are presented with a dish of nuts which comprise two parts (cashews or peanuts) observe how you are instinctively drawn to select the whole, plumpest nut rather than the divided one. Similarly, faced with a whole carrot or one where the base has split into two, we choose the whole carrot. This choice is innate: Nature designs wholes, a combination of shape and substance, and we are part of that design that selects wholes in order to function efficiently.

To illustrate this point at a more material level: a scientist would be interested in the amount of peas required by weight or number as a single portion of vegetable content per meal. Industrial caterers budget along these lines. An artist would be more interested in the arrangement of peas in conjunction with the other components. The one is concerned with content, the other with form or shape. But we need both for overall satisfaction.

There is a world of difference between peas thrown on top of a pile of potatoes, and peas arranged according to how they blend in with, not just the potatoes but also the meat and the carrots. Modern cuisine goes to enormous length to fulfil both criteria, knowing instinctively that digestion begins with the eyes. When a beautifully presented meal, organised along texture, shape and colour, is set in front of us we absorb it like music or a piece of art. This is the "ah" factor, an intrinsic recognition of beauty beyond the formality of description. This is what enables us to assimilate what we are eating beyond the food's material nutrients.

Where there is a "fussy" eater in the family, organising the meal along these lines will often serve the function of persuasion where "words" of wisdom will not. Young children are not always convinced that greens are good for them. One of mine fitted into this category, so a teaspoonful of cabbage nestled between the potato, which she adored, and the carrot, which she liked, would ensure she ate some cabbage. Spinach required more extreme measures: I made soup, laced with butternut, onions and carrots and masses of spinach which I then blended. To this day she adores my spinach soup. She did not like the taste of cabbage, but her objection to spinach was the texture.

- Frozen foods used occasionally or for expedience will do us no harm long term and can be sensible. If I need peas for texture, shape and colour to complement a dish I am serving up in winter I am not going to be able to buy them fresh! It becomes a question of priority – do I want to serve this particular meal with peas or are fresh peas the determining factor?

- Canned vegetables, being hermetically sealed and dead, are best avoided wherever possible. Having said that, I am hard pressed to find a viable substitute for tinned tomatoes. When living in New Zealand, it was the custom on the East Coast of the North Island to harvest vast quantities of tomatoes during the season. The home kitchen became the equivalent of a food factory with the produce being bottled for baked beans, ketchup, soups, purées and sauces. Then there were the nectarines, peaches and pears. I had cupboards stocked from floor to ceiling with bottled produce for use out of season.

- Use only what you need. Bin any leftovers from a meal. They have served their purpose.

COMPOSITION OF VEGETABLES

Vitamins (Section Seven)

Vitamin A is found in most orange / red produce but also in kale, broccoli, spinach and cress.

B vitamins occur in most greens.

Vitamin C is abundant in leafy greens.

Protein

The highest proportion will be found in avocados, peas and broad beans.

Note: Potatoes are often presented as a protein food but potatoes belong to the nightshade family and, bio-dynamically, would be classified a de-natured or false protein. Nightshades – tomatoes, sweet peppers, cayenne pepper, aubergine and tobacco – are stimulants rather than tissue builders. Sufferers from some forms of arthritis may find their symptoms are alleviated if they cut out nightshades from their diet. A macrobiotic diet excludes nightshades absolutely.

Nightshade foods seem to like dairy for balance – hence we add butter, cream or milk to potato; cheese and tomato is a popular combination both in pizza and sandwiches. For a fairly comprehensive treatise on nightshades consult Anne-Marie Colbin's *"Food and Healing"*. Another excellent reference is *"The Macrobiotic Diet"* by Aveline and Michio Kushi.

Carbohydrate is found in variable amounts in all vegetables.

Fats

Avocados have a proportionately higher fat content than other vegetables. Most vegetables contain only a trace or none at all – depending on which part of the plant you are considering.

WHAT TO LOOK FOR WHEN BUYING

ROOTS AND TUBERS

Firmness; and they should be free from cuts made during lifting.

Swedes and turnips, which belong to the Brassica family, should be small.

Late season carrots and parsnips may be woody in the centre – externally they may present a stiff appearance.

The season for home-grown potatoes is May–August. New potatoes are firm and sappy. Main crop potatoes from September onwards are more floury and good for mashing and baking.

BULBS AND STEMS

Onions until last century were classified as an herb not a vegetable. They are invaluable for flavouring savoury dishes and excellent medicinally because they open up the body pores to promote the expulsion of toxins. An ideal remedy for a head cold is a large dish of cooked onions prior to going to bed. A peeled cut onion will attract germs so only use them freshly prepared.

- Tight round onions are pungent.
- Look for tight necks. Reject any that are sprouting
- You can cook spring onions – briefly, such as stir-frying.

Leeks – beware late season leeks (i.e. spring and summer) when they may have solid inedible centres prior to seeding.

Celery – look for firm roots.

Asparagus – the home-produced is most flavoursome and is usually fiercesomely expensive. Look for tight tip-buds.

BRASSICAS

Always check the root base. If it is nicotine-stained it is stale. If slimy, it is rotten!

Sprouts, Cauliflower, Broccoli – should be tight, firm and fresh looking. They are a disaster when yellowing. Even organically grown ones!!

Cabbage

White cabbage is traditional for coleslaw.

Chinese leaves should be crisp and eaten raw.

Crinkly leaved Savoys are best steamed.

All should be firm at heart.

Spring greens will take to steaming / boiling.

LEAVES

Spinach should be vibrant and squeaky.

Salad Greens need eating immediately. Iceberg stores better than Butterhead or Webbs. Webbs and Cos are more flavoursome. The whole lettuce is better than the packaged leaves so much in favour now – check they haven't been chemically sprayed to stop them wilting in the packet. Best of all, grow your own!

Chicory – leaf tips should be yellow; they turn green and bitter if exposed.

Watercress makes a lovely soup and is an excellent source of iron. Store in a fridge.

FRUIT AND FLOWER VEGETABLES

These should be glossy, firm and plump.

Aubergine should be glossy, firm, and dark purple.

Avocados should be gently yielding but not squashy.

Courgettes – small slim courgettes are tastier than the larger, fatter ones.

Cucumber should be firm all over. If the taste is bitter this is a sign of self rather than cross-pollination.

Peppers – the red variety is sweeter than the green.

Sweet corn should be densely packed, sappy, and pale, creamy yellow in colour. Dark yellow is a sign of ageing and the kernel will be tough and floury at the centre. Avoid salting during the cooking process to prevent toughening. I buy only organic sweet corn because I cannot be certain the non-organic ones, particularly those from the USA, have not been genetically modified. I apply the same rule to soya and soya products.

Tomatoes if soft can be woolly. Very few nowadays possess flavour.

FUNGI

There are many varieties of mushroom available. Oyster and field mushrooms make a change from cup or button varieties. I like chestnut mushrooms for flavour and firm texture.

STORING VEGETABLES

Store roots out of direct light, preferably in a vegetable rack or basket.

Potatoes should be kept in brown paper bags to prevent greening. Never eat green potatoes: the green is an indication of solanine (an alkaloid) content and is toxic.

Salad vegetables, ideally, should be eaten within 2 days of purchase. They will store for approximately 7 days in a refrigerator but bear in mind the vitamin benefits of all vegetable produce deteriorate from the moment they are picked and the more ephemeral the fruit or vegetable (salad leaves and strawberries) the more rapid the loss.

Tropical fruits such as mangoes, oranges and lemons – store as for root vegetables.

Temperate fruits – grapes, apples, plums, cherries and pears – store as for root vegetables or in a refrigerator.

Dried fruit: keep in a dark, airy cupboard in airtight containers for up to 6 months.

PREPARING VEGETABLES AND FRUIT

Gather a selection of produce onto the kitchen table and check for compatibility: size, shape, texture, taste and colour.

Wash thoroughly under cold running water and drain. If necessary, pat dry with a clean cloth or tea towel.

Trim the ends of stalks, discard the outer tough leaves of brassicas.

Use sharp knives and a clean board. I use wooden boards because I do not find plastic or laminates particularly suitable for food preparation; it scours easily and blunts knives. Wooden boards can be scrubbed with salt to ensure they are hygienic, and their efficacy has withstood the test of time.

Ensure the working surface is a comfortable height for you. Arms need to feel free and flexible not rigid or pushed up into the shoulders. Standing with the legs hip-width apart grounds the body and supports the upper body's activity. Stand so that you can see what you are doing without having to keep your neck bent. The neck should be able to lengthen up into the back of the head, with the chin drawn in not down. Shoulders relax down; if they move up exhale slowly and fully, inviting the tips of the shoulder blades to draw the backs of the shoulders down towards the back of the waist.

As you work tune into your breathing pattern occasionally. Develop a comfortable exhalation as you move towards the food and relax to the incoming breath as you move away from the food. The inhalation should be passive. Let it come in rather than drawing it in. Subtle energy (prana) comes to you as a gift via the inhalation; you transport this energy into the food via your nervous system on the exhalation. In between the exhalations and inhalations there is a slight pause, a resting period when nothing is going on. The pause links the two, so the breathing becomes smooth, regular and moves in a circular pattern not like a piston. It is soft, unforced, and soothing.

The intellect quietens and you are drawn in with what you are doing until you are totally absorbed. You are entranced but at no time are you unaware of what you are doing – if anything your senses are heightened. You are more likely to be aware of the postman's approach before you hear the letters falling through the letterbox than not hear the postman at all. You will however find it difficult, if not impossible, to keep track of an ongoing debate on the radio.

Cut or chop according to the direction of growth. Always cut away from you rather than towards you because this ensures you are directing energy into, rather than drawing it away from, the food. As you bring the knife back your hand makes a horizontal movement like the arm of a rotary machine rather than the linear movement of a saw. This ensures an uninterrupted process. You remain connected with the implement and vegetable – working with, rather than going against, the food. Energetically it makes sense to go with rather than against the flow of the current because we are looking for harmony not resistance.

Broccoli – cut the stem as close to the head of the florets as possible. Trim the base and cut away the outer sheath if it is tough / woody. Slice the prepared stem thinly on the diagonal to ensure it cooks within the same length of time as the florets. Separate the florets and cook them whole.

Bulbs – round vegetables or fruits such as onions, swedes, turnips, pumpkin, melon or squash: cut in half through the north-south polarity, then place cut side down and cut again north-south in slices.

Round cabbages – always cut through north–south; place the cut side down and cut through again to allow easy removal of the core. Cabbage may be cooked quartered or, if you prefer it shredded, slice the quarters into thin strips.

Carrots, and parsnips – cut diagonally into strips rather than in rounds. If you want chunks, make the first cut longitudinally. Then cut diagonally, working from north to south.

Celery, courgettes and leeks – trim both ends and then cut longitudinally from top to bottom before slicing diagonally or across.

For dicing (e.g. runner beans) – after trimming both ends, keep all the lengths together and cut crosswise.

HINTS ON COOKING VEGETABLES

Most vegetables can be eaten raw but not potato as it is virtually indigestible.

Cook greens for as short a time as possible in a minimal amount of water.

Steaming or baking is preferable to boiling on most occasions to ensure maximum nutritional uptake.

Cauliflower, sprouts, leeks, celery and asparagus take better to steaming than boiling as this is a gentler form of cooking. Kale on the other hand tastes sweeter for being boiled, as does dark green cabbage.

Vitamin C is destroyed by heat and oxidation.

B vitamins are light sensitive and are soluble in water.

Sodium bicarbonate may enhance the colour of your cabbage but it will murder the vitamin C and B content of your food, so better not use it!

Root vegetables take about 20 minutes to cook, carrots less.

If you must use it, add salt after cooking; cooking in salted water ensures up to 50% of the iron content is leached out of the vegetable.

Scrub vegetables in preference to peeling. If the produce is not organic the scrubbing should be brisk and under warm running water to eliminate surface chemical residues. A scrubbing utensil made from vegetable fibres, such as coconut, is preferable to plastic to minimise damage to the skin.

Handle and prepare the produce as little, and as close to mealtimes, as possible.

Keep calm, clear, positive thoughts flowing through your head during preparation times. Go with the flow! And remember, the entire world is composed of energy engaged in a continuous interchange. Put into your food mentally what you expect to get out of it.

Steaming – use a perforated stainless-steel steamer over a pan of boiling water and ensure a well-fitting lid. Full instructions on usage and cooking times are included with electric steamers.

Boiling – root vegetables should be cooked by putting them in cold water and bringing them to the boil but all greens should be added to boiling water, to retain colour and nutrients. Use the residual water for stock.

Braising – either in the oven or by simmering on a hob – fry a little chopped onion or garlic in ghee or olive oil until soft. Add the finely-sliced vegetables and lightly fry. Add the stock (water / wine / juice). Add a few herbs / spices. Simmer until tender.

Roasting / Baking – most suited to roots, onions or tubers. Brush the prepared vegetables with oil. Season. Bake in a roasting dish in a hot oven until tender. Potatoes can be baked in their skins on a baking tray without any oil if preferred. Pierce the skins in several places with the end of a sharp knife to prevent them exploding in the oven.

Stir-frying – cut the vegetables very thinly. Heat a combination of butter and oil in a heavy fry pan or, preferably, a wok. Add garlic or herbs. Add the vegetables and stir continuously for a few minutes and then add liquid of choice (about 6 tbs per 450 gm of vegetable). Boil rapidly until liquid is reduced by half.

Grilling – brush vegetables with oil / melted ghee and place under a hot grill until tender.

Uncooked – wash thoroughly under cold running water. Scrub to remove the dirt. Slice or chop as required according to the direction of growth.

SECTION SIX

BAKING

Bread, Cakes,
Puddings and Desserts

Baking connects with our emotions. It is the most intimate aspect of cooking. From bread making to pastry, crumble toppings or scones, we are handling the food more directly than when we are chopping vegetables, stirring a sauce, basting a joint or grilling a fish. The latter involve the intermediary of implements to a much greater degree and this separates us from direct contact with ingredients.

Apart from eating there can be no closer relationship with food than running fingers through ingredients to mix, blend or knead. We are deeply involved through this continuity of touch. There is an uninterrupted interaction on an energetic level which is personal. Our attention is held, absorbed into and by the process; we are focused and energised and this human energy is communicated into the substance.

I muse over the proprietary term "hand-baked" and wonder how much economy of truth is employed here by the catering industry. The modern obsession with germs precludes human touch "contaminating" the food. Handling invariably comes with a fingered plastic sheath separating handler from food which, if the hands putting on the gloves are unwashed to begin with, is not necessarily as hygienic as it implies!

So much industrial catering relies on machinery for mass production, which depersonalises the process and is akin to spectator sport. There can be no interaction between living substance and machines. With the best will in the world, those employed in food factories are employed primarily for their labour not an ability to empathise with either the ingredients or anonymous consumers.

On an intrinsic level these foods seem to lack soul quality – which possibly explains why, at the weekly Saturday coffee morning in the Northumbrian village of Wooler, there is a near-stampede to strip bare the tables of home-baked produce. Arrive 15 minutes after the hall opens and you are guaranteed disappointment.

On a subtle level "home-baked" is instinctively preferred to "factory-made" and is why the food industry has to bombard consumers with an increasingly sophisticated mixture of additives to entice jaded appetites into buying "ready-made". A frequently heard complaint from several acquaintances who buy ready-made meals is that they all possess a "sameness" of taste.

A favourite gambit is that buying ready-made saves time in busy lives, the implication being that cooking is a chore that distracts us from "real work". The paradox is that designer kitchens have never been more popular. One woman I know well has recently renovated her Victorian terrace with most of the expense lavished on the kitchen. It looks brilliant and one year on, brand- new. This kitchen is a fashion statement where the oven is used mostly for heating up prepared foods, rarely for cooking; the fridge is stocked with snack foods and pre-packed and not a fresh vegetable in sight. Fine, but for the fact that her daily mantra is one of feeling stressed and needing to continuously "chill out" – which she does by snacking incessantly and drinking copious cappuccinos......!

A diet that consists mostly of takeaway and ready-made foods buys us time at the cost of "life quality" which can become seriously compromised. How much mental stress would be alleviated if we paused to take time with our nourishment? On the continent the British are disparaged (perhaps unfairly) for their uncivilised attitudes towards food. We are perceived as scoffers – people who down food rather than people who enjoy eating – rather like geese being fattened for pâté. It is no accident that the sandwich was an English invention. Yet the sandwich bar is one area of the catering industry that remains predominantly hands-on and its products can be personalised, particularly in the smaller delis that have become fashionable in our towns and villages.

At the beginning of this book I stated that my mother would not cook, which is not to say she could not cook. Later in life when she had grandchildren she would occasionally bake for them. She possessed long, cool fingers that made wonderful pastry, and once a year she would make a vast quantity of mince pies and freeze them. She did this not just to economise on time. Watching her make pastry was fascinating. Pastry making requires light handling and my mother, always uneasy with her sense of touch, developed this into an art form: her fingering the ingredients bore the hallmarks of the air guitarist. It was more a gift than a knack and to this day her grandchildren remain convinced their grandmother's pastry was unsurpassable.

Batters and cakes also make for a close relationship with the ingredients if not in quite the same way as pastry, scone or bread making. Tucking a mixing bowl under one arm is akin to holding an infant and the rhythm of a wooden spoon creaming and blending is as soothing as a lullaby. I often sing whilst baking. It makes for light labour and timelessness. There is a lovely Northumbrian girdle scone recipe called "Singing Hinnies", so named because the batter sizzling on the hob is akin to singing. I first came across them some eighteen years ago when visiting the Belford Craft Gallery in North Northumberland where the Atkin family combined local arts with a pottery and tea room. Such was the popularity of Mrs. Atkin's hinnies she could have found herself doing little else but mass-produce them.

These Northumberland scones are rather like flat Eccles cakes without the sugar. Hinny (Honey) is a term of endearment in the Northeast and essentially these are one of your granny's "about-a-handful" recipes – but try these quantities to make 6 tea-plate-sized scones.

SINGING HINNIES

250 gm plain flour

125 gm best butter

¼ tsp baking powder

Pinch of sea salt

Handful of currants

¼ pint milk (sour or buttermilk if available, though fresh whole milk is fine)

Mix the flour, salt and baking powder in a bowl and rub in the butter, taking care to leave the butter in tiny lumps. Throw in the currants and mix with the milk to obtain a traditional scone consistency. Divide into six parts and roll into balls by hand, using plenty of flour. Then roll each out into a thin, roughly-round shape and cook on a "girdle" or heavy bottomed fry pan until golden brown and speckly. This is when they sing – when the little lumps of butter bubble through and sizzle. Turn once with a fish slice or a pair of "singing hinny hands" (roughly the equivalent of 2 fish slices!).

They should be crisp on the outside and soft on the inside when done. Speed is the essence – they need to be eaten immediately, served up hot with butter and home-made strawberry or raspberry jam.

When making traditional scones I tend to blend the yoghurt or sour milk into the dry mixture by hand. Rather than use a rolling pin, I lightly press out the dough by hand and use a small glass, or a metal pastry cutter, to obtain the individual rounds.

I use half the quantity of butter to SR flour and (in the absence of buttermilk) a blend of natural bio yoghurt and milk sufficient to obtain a soft dough. I bake the scones in the centre of a pre-heated oven (Gas 6 / 200 C) for approximately 15–20 minutes.

Nutritional Note: I always use butter in cooking, never margarine, which is an artificial concoction marketed as a healthy alternative. (Section Seven)

I make cakes entirely by hand unless dealing with extra-large quantities when I will sometimes initiate the creaming process in a food blender and then turn the mixture into my customary stoneware mixing bowl before proceeding to the next stage. I prefer the feel of stoneware to plastic, it is more substantial for one thing – more comfortable to hug under an arm – and consensus amongst friends suggests the leftover raw cake mixture tastes better for having had a finger trailed round a stoneware bowl rather than a plastic one. I have found finger-licking-leftover-raw-cake-mixture accompanies one through life. Mother initiates the children in the practice and later, in the absence of grandchildren, resumes it herself as if there had never been a lapse. This is one raw food that in terms of comfort eating competes with the cooked version on equal terms though too much of any good thing can induce nausea.

I also prefer to whip egg whites by hand, using a copper basin and a balloon whisk for speed and efficacy. The resultant volume is copious and light –whereas a blender tends to render a denser heavier texture in my experience.

BREAD

Modern bread is basically a mixture of strong flour, yeast and water, or water and milk. Recipes are often found on the flour packet and tend to work well, as do those found in any comprehensive cookery book. By far the best book I have come across on bread making is *"The Sunday Times Book of Bread"*[1]. It covers the history of bread; describes bread-making techniques; and an entire section is devoted to recipes submitted by professional cooks such as Elizabeth David, Doris Grant and Jane Grigson – to name a few.

The smell of bread baking is irresistible, as supermarkets have discovered to their advantage. Nowadays home bread-making machines are quite popular since all one has to do is pop in the ingredients and leave everything to the machine. However, once the novelty has worn off, the machine is often relegated to a cupboard never again to see the light of day. Though I have friends who swear by them, I could never quite get used to the hole in the bottom of the loaf when I tried a machine; and I found the mechanised processing experience disturbingly unsatisfying.

The hand-baked process is very simple and not necessarily as time consuming as a recipe might suggest. I suspect that most people are put off making their own bread because of this perception. I organise regular bread making around my day, so that whilst I am waiting for the bread to rise I'll work on my computer or on my yoga mat. After a while you mentally adjust so that you instinctively know when it is time to attend to the dough.

Coming home at the end of a busy day to make bread could seem like the proverbial straw that broke the camel's back but kneading bread is a relaxation technique quite as efficacious as the gin and tonic. It is guaranteed to take tension out of the neck and upper back, with the bonus that there is fresh bread on the breakfast table (Health Warning: kneading bread can become addictive!)

I like to use organic flours whether I'm making white, brown or granary loaves and for personal preference I use fresh yeast. For some inexplicable reason I find fresh yeast yields me better results than dried yeast. Supermarkets are willing to give you fresh yeast if you apply to the home baking section. I tend to use rather more than is suggested in most recipes I have looked at.

[2] *"The Sunday Times Book of Bread"* by Michael Bateman and Heather Maisner. Published in 1982 by the Rodale Press, Aylesbury

KNEADING BREAD

This can turn into a very peaceful meditative experience.

Stand with feet hip-width apart and allow the weight of the body to release down through the pelvis into the feet.

Keep the knees soft and simply let the feet be absorbed by gravity into the floor.

Tune into your breathing rhythm and on each exhalation release the weight into the ground.

Then, as you receive the next incoming breath, allow the spine to quietly lengthen up out of the pelvis towards the back of the head. To ensure this happens, on the exhalation take care to relax down into the feet rather than collapsing into the softened knees. Collapsing equates with abandoning responsibility for your self!

Gradually the breathing rate will slow down and deepen and you will flow with it both mentally and physically, as you continue to release the weight into the floor and lighten up on the inhalation.

To knead the bread, use your dominant hand, pushing the dough away from you on an exhalation. Use the heel of the hand to push and allow the fingertips of the other hand to collect fold and return the dough to the active hand.

As you settle into the rhythm, allow the body to flow into and out of the movement. You will find the rocking motion soothing.

Keep the knees soft and the feet firmly grounded.

Keep the shoulders relaxed and mentally stay with what you are doing. Be involved.

You will be surprised how quickly 15 minutes pass, by which time the dough will feel quite elastic and ready for resting and rising.

And you will feel fresh and invigorated, ready for a new task during the waiting period, or simply relax with your feet up and enjoy some music or a good book.

There is really very little that can go wrong with bread making once you have accustomed yourself to the ratio of the basic ingredients and it lends itself to experimentation in all sorts of ways, from substitution to addition. Once you have gained confidence in the art of bread-making, the imagination knows no bounds, and you will find your friends encouraging.

SIMPLE LARGE
WHITE WHEATEN LOAF

2 heaped cups strong flour plus
1 cup for kneading

25 gm fresh yeast / 1 sachet
dried yeast

350 ml or 1⅓ cups water

1 level tsp sea salt

1 dsp Demerara sugar

25 gm or a large walnut sized
piece of butter (optional). I find
butter helps to retain moisture
in the bread.

Sunflower oil

In a large mixing bowl combine the flour, salt and butter and place in the warming drawer of an oven set to (Gas 2 / 150 C). If you do not have a warming drawer any warm place, such as an airing cupboard, will suffice.

Heat the water to a comfortable hand-hot temperature, pour into a smaller mixing bowl and dissolve the sugar. Stir in the yeast until it has dissolved and becomes active.

Remove the flour bowl from the oven, make a well in the centre and pour in the yeast mixture, sprinkling a little flour over the top. After a few minutes, mix thoroughly with a wooden spoon. The mixture should be soft but not too tacky. Add more liquid if necessary. Don't worry if the butter hasn't been completely worked in because the kneading process will resolve that. If you are too heavy-handed with the water simply add more flour.

Turn out onto a floured board and knead for 15–20 minutes adding more flour as required.

Pour a little sunflower oil into the mixing bowl and return the kneaded dough, turning it over so that the surface is well oiled. Cover with cling film or a damp cloth and set aside in a warm place to rise until it is double in size. The time varies. I find 30 minutes is ample time for this rising, possibly because I use plenty of yeast. Depending on the season and overall temperature of your kitchen rising times will vary. It can take up to an hour if it is a very cold day so check after ½ an hour.

Punch the dough down and turn it back onto the floured board. Lightly knead for a few minutes and then place it in a large, oiled bread tin. You can use either 1 large tin or 2 small ones. Sometimes I divide the dough into 2 balls and place them side by side in a large tin. Leave in a warm place to rise just above the top of the tin.

Heat the oven (Gas 8 / 220 C).

Bake in the centre of the oven for 15 minutes, and then turn down the temperature (Gas 6 / 200 C) and bake for a further 15 minutes.

If I use two smaller tins, 20 minutes in total at the higher setting is sufficient to cook the bread.

Turn out of the tin and check that the loaf is thoroughly cooked by tapping the base with your knuckles. It should sound hollow. If you suspect it requires a little more cooking, place it back in the oven upside down, leave the heat on for another five minutes and then turn the oven off. If it is cooked, finish off by putting it back in the oven, upside down, with the heat turned off. Leave to cool for a few minutes before removing from the oven and placing on a wire tray. A finished white loaf should be golden on the outside.

If you prefer to make bread rolls, divide the dough equally into 10 / 12 balls and place on an oiled baking tray. Flatten them slightly and leave to rise. They will take approximately 10–15 minutes to cook.

Additions and substitutions

To create a glazed effect, brush the top of the loaf with a little milk or soya milk prior to the second rising.

Add a good handful or more of mixed seeds to the flour at the outset.

Sunflower, pumpkin, sesame, poppy, black onion and linseed make a good mix.

A small handful of raisins and / or pre-soaked chopped apricots can be substituted for seeds or used in combination with seeds for a sweeter loaf.

A tablespoonful of chopped stoned olives and sun-dried tomatoes make for a Mediterranean flavour.

Cooked, chopped onions added to the flour give an interesting flavour and make a good accompaniment for savoury starters such as soups or pâtés.

White bread tastes lovely and chewy if a good handful of cooked long grain rice is stirred into the warmed flour prior to adding the yeast, and it makes delicious toast.

Substituting some of the water content with an egg beaten with a little warm milk will enrich bread. I often used this when my children were younger.

Substitute some of the wheat content with other cereals such as barley, rye, millet or oat flakes. Use 1 part cereal flakes to 5 parts strong wheat flour.

Cooked sweet corn kernels, plus a handful of maize meal (polenta) and a good knob of butter, combined with wheat flour lends an interesting texture as well as flavour.

THE ESOTERIC ASPECTS OF GRAINS

Wheat, rich in calcium salts, is representative of the Earth which gives us form or shape.

Rye, rich in potassium salts, is representative of water and lends us tone which is why rye products, such as rye crispbreads, are popular with slimmers. Rye will tone muscle whereas wheat will promote flab!

Barley, rich in silicic acid, is representative of air. In winter, in the relative absence of light, barley bread is a metaphor for stored light.

Oats, rich in magnesium salts, is representative of fire.

If you are of melancholic disposition you may be drawn to the fire of oats for balance. Cholerics on the other hand would be better taking to wheat or rye, to weight them down (stop them flying off the handle!)

OAT BREAD

100 gm porridge oats

250 ml hot milk

200 ml hand-hot water

1 tbs clear honey

25 gm fresh yeast or
1 sachet dried yeast

500 gm strong wholewheat
flour

50 gm oatgerm

1 tsp sea salt

25 gm butter

1 egg (optional)

Place the oats and scalded milk in a small bowl and leave for 20 minutes.

Place the hand-hot water in a small basin, add the honey, stir until dissolved, sprinkle on the yeast and leave until frothy,

Place the flour, oatgerm and salt in a mixing bowl, rub in the butter, make a well in the centre and add the oats, egg and yeast liquid (if no egg is used a little more liquid may be required – use discretion – the dough needs to be pliable, soft, not tacky).

Mix until the dough begins to leave the side of the bowl.

Turn out onto a floured board and knead until the dough feels firm. Place this back in the mixing bowl and cover with oiled cling film or a clean, damp tea towel. Leave to rise until about double in size – approximately 30–45 minutes.

Oil 2 small 450 gm loaf tins. Divide the dough in half and shape into loaves. Leave to rise again until the dough reaches almost to the top of the tins (about an hour).

Place the tins on a baking sheet in the centre of a pre-heated oven (Gas 7 / 210 C) and bake for 30–35 minutes. To test, remove from the tin and tap the base. When cooked, the bread will sound hollow. (If necessary, place the loaves, upside down, on the baking sheet and bake for a few minutes longer). Cool on a wire rack.

GRANARY BAPS
Makes 6 large baps

445 gm granary flour, warmed

25 gm fresh yeast / 1 sachet
dried yeast

110 gm finely grated carrot
(grated carrot keeps the bread
light and moist)

1 tbs black treacle

30 gm melted butter

280 ml hand-hot water

Beaten egg to glaze (optional)

Cracked wheat (optional)

Mix the treacle and melted butter with 280 ml hand-hot water and sprinkle on the yeast, setting it aside to froth. Mix the flour and salt in a mixing bowl and stir in the carrot. Add the yeast and water mixture and stir to obtain a soft, but not sticky, dough, adding a little more water or flour as necessary.

Turn onto a floured work surface and knead for 10–15 minutes.

Put into an oiled bowl, cover with oiled cling-film or a damp cloth and leave in a warm place until doubled in size.

Knock back the dough and divide into 6. Shape and place on a greased baking tray (use oil rather than butter because the salt content in butter can cause the bread to stick). Leave in a warm place until doubled in size.

If using egg, brush the surface and sprinkle on a little cracked wheat.

Heat oven (Gas 6 / 200 C) and bake for approximately 25 minutes. Cool on a wire tray.

RYEBREAD
Makes 1 large cake

2 cups rye flour

1 cup wholemeal flour

¾ cup treacle or light syrup
(rice or corn syrup)

2 cups buttermilk warmed

1 tsp baking powder

15gm fresh yeast or 1 tsp dried yeast

¾ tsp sea salt

Soak the yeast in the warm buttermilk.

Liberally oil 1 deep cake tin.

Set the oven to Gas1 or the first setting on an electric oven.

Mix all the ingredients together in a large bowl, pour into the tin and place in a bain-marie (a roasting dish part-filled with hot water) and bake for 3 hours.

Turn out onto a wire rack to cool.

This bread keeps well in an airtight container in the fridge for up to 10 days.

Serve thinly sliced with butter.

MUFFINS

Courtesy of my daughter, who was interested in re-visiting her birthplace, I made a long-overdue return to New Zealand in 2003 where I was introduced to muffins, – a delicacy I sampled in practically every place we visited over a period of 3 weeks.

The trick to successful muffin-making is speed and under-mixing. The following are two recipes casually thrown my way by an old friend during our reunion at a local café.

CHEESE MUFFINS
Makes 12 large muffins

2 cups grated hard cheese

½ cup SR flour plus ½ tsp sea salt

1 cup milk

1 free-range egg, beaten

Pinch cayenne

Mix everything together lightly, pour into greased muffin tins and bake for 10–12 minutes (Gas 7 / 210 C).

CRUNCHY LEMON MUFFINS

2 cups SR flour

¾ cup sugar

75 gm butter softened

1 cup milk

1 free-range egg beaten

Grated rind 1 large organic lemon

Combine all the ingredients as above and cook (Gas 6 / 200 C) for 10 minutes.

Turn out onto a cooling rack and, whilst hot, drizzle with ¼ cup sugar stirred into ¼ cup lemon juice.

Eat fresh when cool. Accompanied with a large cappuccino or mochaccino this is truly decadent, undeniably wickedly delicious and not for the abstemious.

A recipe for **Bran Muffins** (makes approximately 10) came courtesy of an American friend who, whilst living in Northumberland, introduced us to American delicacies but they are dissimilar in taste and texture from other kinds of muffins I have enjoyed. (Section Two – Breakfasts)

CAKES, PUDDINGS AND DESSERTS

Sweet foods flood us with memories of childhood. We talk about sweet memories. An image of a child conjures up sweetness and we are flooded with feelings of tenderness. There is an innate sense of wanting to protect and cosset the young from the harsher realities of what we as adults make of Life, whether that young is a tender new shoot needing shelter from extreme weather, an animal in need of rearing or a human baby. In war time seeing an "innocent" child in the rescuing arms of a battle-worn soldier moves us profoundly. Our hearts are flooded with compassion and briefly at one with Reality, God, Truth, Love, whatever we recognise as Wholeness. In that moment we cease to be fragmented and feel complete. Yoga sums up this single Truth in three simple words: I am That.

The innocence of the inexperienced young is haunting, elusive, because we have lost the art of simply being in whatever we are doing. Somehow we have separated out, stepped back and we transfer from beings into doings. Our mental processes create the illusion I am no longer That, That is an Object and I am a Subject. A chocolate mousse melting on the tongue, a morsel of "angel-light" cake, ice cream, is instantly absorbed into our very essence and we are transported back to that other reality: I am That.

So sweet foods serve a very real and useful purpose in bringing us back to our original state of being, that is One-ness. Unfortunately we have substituted illusion for reality to such a degree, moving further and further away from our Truth, that we require more and more reminders to take us back, and our need for sweetness can develop into cravings or addictions. What was an occasional relished treat becomes a requirement.

In earlier times, springtime heralded the New Year and festivals celebrated this with cakes and sweetmeats such as simnel cakes, raisin and almond sweetmeats, and other such sticky, spicy goodies. Indeed sugar was originally termed a spice, to be used sparingly. Nowadays, on average, we consume in a fortnight what only a hundred years or so ago we consumed in a year. That is a prodigious rise!

The sweet part of a plant is for the most part found in the flower – the nectar – and carried in the perfume. It is usually the most ethereal aspect, though some plants such as carrots, parsnips, liquorice and beets carry a more mineralised sugar in the root. Others, such as aniseed, will bear it in the stem, as does the cane from which we used to derive most of our sugar.

On an intrinsic or spiritual level the purpose of sweet foods is to assist us in re-discovering our reality. As children we were unconscious of our state of being. At some stage in our development we lost this "innocence" and our purpose as adults is to regain consciously our at-oneness or state of being. Sugar's purpose is an aid to Consciousness, not an end in itself. Ancient religious texts talk about a Land of Milk and Honey and it is interesting how many latter-day gurus advocate for their adherents a diet that leans heavily towards milk and sugar. But sugar dependency, like any other dependency, enslaves rather than liberates.

Back on the more Earthly plane, the western diet usually includes a sweet after a savoury main course. During the Middle-Ages, sweetmeats were literally meats sweetened with fruits such as raisins, dates or figs, and were often accompanied by what we would call a sweet custard. Today we use sweet chutneys and jellies to accompany curries and game.

Yorkshire pudding was originally a regional dish that supplemented the meat component of a meal and, though not sweetened with sugar, contained milk. Sometimes the main meal commenced with a large plate of Yorkshire pudding covered in onion gravy, which was then followed by the meat, potatoes and greens. A family friend of my parents' generation ate Yorkshire pudding every weekday on coming home from work. What was unusual about this was his habit of smothering his pudding with a large spoonful of golden syrup and then pouring on the thick onion gravy! Maybe a throwback to mediaeval genes?

Both pudding and dessert will counterbalance the savoury aspect of our diet. Many people, particularly slimmers, will incorporate a piece of fruit. Personally I prefer to eat fruit by itself and, unless it is a banana, never with carbohydrate, because to do so will encourage fermentation in the gut. Often a piece of fruit after a savoury main course will feel less satisfying than dessert or a piece of cake. If there is a tendency to reach for the chocolates for snacking during the evening after dinner, a little dessert might be a better choice.

Men, in my experience, tend to relish puddings more than their female counterparts, so I usually offer one alongside a lighter dessert. I have no idea why this is the case and I have had many suggestions ranging from "it takes them back to their childhood", "it reminds them of mother" to "they've got bigger appetites". None of these is a satisfactory explanation since women also have mothers and childhoods, and I have known several women with decidedly larger appetites than their men folk. And many younger men will not have experienced during their childhoods the puddings that were once commonplace both at school and home up until the 1960s.

It remains a mystery I will happily cater to since it produces such delight in my male dinner guests. Besides, puddings are simple to make and I am a slave to an easy life!

BASIC SPONGE PUDDING
Serves 4–6 generous helpings or 8 moderate portions

Weigh 2 large free-range eggs and use this result as the standard measure for all the other ingredients, except the vanilla essence.

SR flour

Butter

Natural cane caster sugar

A few drops vanilla essence

Grease or oil a 1 litre / 2 pint pudding basin. If using a plastic container there is no need to grease it.

Cream the butter and sugar until soft and fluffy with a wooden spoon.

Beat the eggs and add gradually to the creamed mixture, beating until completely blended. Sift in the flour, folding lightly with a metal spoon. Add a few drops of natural vanilla essence.

Place a heaped tablespoon or more of jam in the bottom of the pudding basin. Spoon the sponge mixture over the top. It should reach no further than $^{2}/_{3}$rd up the sides of the basin. Cover with foil and steam for 1¾–2 hours.

Turn out onto a pre-heated plate or shallow dish and serve with plenty of fresh custard. I usually make about 900 ml with a minimal amount of sugar. If there is any left over, chop in some fresh banana and serve up chilled the next day as Banana Custard; or stir in some stewed apple to make Apple Custard.

A bonus is that any leftover sponge can be put back into its basin and re-steamed for 20–30 minutes the next day. I have to say, however, that I rarely have any of this pudding left over!

Variations on the Basic Sponge

Combine 1tbs good cocoa to the flour and, if necessary, add a little milk to obtain the same consistency as the original sponge.

Add 1 heaped tsp dry ginger to the flour for a ginger sponge.

Add some mixed dried fruit in the same ratio to the rest of the sponge ingredients, and add a little milk if necessary.

Use chopped natural preserved cherries in place of the dried fruit.

Use cherries and replace 1tbs flour with 1tbs ground almonds. Add ¼ tsp baking powder and substitute pure almond essence for vanilla.

Add the grated rind of 1 lemon plus juice of ½ lemon.

Alternatives to Jam

Golden syrup

Toffee fudge spread

Ginger jam or rhubarb and ginger jam together with the ginger sponge

Apricot purée made from soaked dried apricots blended in a food processor

Cold stewed apple – this goes very well with ginger sponge

Sugar-free pear and apple spread

Sugar-free jam / marmalade

Marmalade

Lemon, lime or orange curd

Alternatives to custard

White sauce made from cornflour rather than custard powder goes well with chocolate sponge.

Chocolate sauce made from cocoa and cornflour, or cocoa and custard powder.

Cream, yoghurt, crème fraiche, fromage fraîs

VANILLA FROMAGE FRAÎS
Serves 4 – 6 people

In a mixing bowl empty a large pot of fromage fraîs, add natural cane caster sugar to taste, a few drops of vanilla essence, and whip with a balloon whisk. It is almost impossible to buy full fat fromage fraîs these days, which is a pity because the fat free product tastes mean. Sugar improves it. Organic producers tend to supply the genuine article if you can get hold of it. This sweet can be served up on its own or as an accompaniment for soft fresh fruits, fruit salads, slices of lime drizzle cake.

LEMON TART

Line a 23 / 24 cm. flan dish with sweet shortcrust pastry and bake blind for approximately 25 minutes. (To bake blind see below: Curd Cheesecake)

Combine 3 eggs, 1 egg yolk, the juice of 3 lemons and 1 orange, 160 ml double cream and 150 gm natural cane caster sugar. Beat well to ensure sugar is dissolved (it should look fluffy) and pour into the pastry case. Bake until the filling is firm, in the centre of a cool oven (Gas 3 / 170 C). Test after 30 minutes.

LIME DRIZZLE CAKE

Finely grated rind 2 limes

175 gm natural caster sugar

225 gm soft butter

3–4 organic eggs, beaten

250 gm SR flour

For the syrup

Juice of 2 limes

100 gm unrefined / natural cane caster sugar

Heat the oven to (Gas 4 / 180 C).

Grease and line with greaseproof paper a 1kg loaf tin.

Mix the lime rind with the caster sugar, add the butter, and cream until fluffy.

Add the eggs a little at a time and blend with the creamed mixture.

Sift the flour and fold this into the mixture with a metal spoon. Turn into the tin, smooth the top and bake for 1¼ hours or until golden brown and springy to the touch.

Meanwhile make the syrup by slowly heating the lime juice with the sugar until it dissolves. When the cake is baked, turn it out onto a wire cooling rack, make several slashes diagonally across the top with a sharp knife, and pour the syrup over. Sprinkle on a little extra caster sugar and leave to cool.

If serving as a sweet I use vanilla fromage fraîs or yoghurt as an accompaniment.

CHEESECAKE

For the base

1½ cups digestive biscuit crumbs mixed with 3 tbs melted butter and 2 tbs raw cane sugar.

For the filling

2 organic eggs, separated

½ cup sugar

1 tbs lemon juice

Grated rind one unwaxed lemon

½ tsp natural vanilla essence

500 gm curd or soft cream cheese cut into pieces

Base: Press into the base of a loose-bottomed 27cm cake tin and bake for 5 minutes (Gas 3 / 170 C). Cool.

Filling: In a blender process half the cheese, the egg yolks, sugar, juice, rind, and vanilla essence. When smooth add the remaining cheese gradually. Blend again. Whisk the egg whites, preferably in a copper for ease, until they form stiff peaks and carefully fold into the cheese mixture. Spoon over the cooled biscuit base and bake until golden and set – approximately 45–60 minutes (Gas 3 / 170 C). Cool before removing from the tin and easing onto a plate.

Topping: Blend 1 cup sour cream with 1 tbs organic caster sugar and ¼ tsp vanilla essence. Spread evenly over the top of the cooled cheesecake and chill for up to ½ an hour before serving.

CURD CHEESECAKE
Serves 8

For the filling

450 gm curd cheese

½ cup double cream

2 large organic eggs plus 1 organic egg yolk

75 gm unrefined caster sugar

Finely grated rind 1 organic or unwaxed lemon

Juice ½ lemon

Heat the oven (Gas 5 / 190 C).

Line a fluted 23 cm loose-bottomed flan tin with sweet shortcrust pastry. Prick the base of the pastry case, line with baking parchment and fill with dried beans. Bake for 15 minutes. Transfer onto a wire rack, remove the beans and parchment, and allow it to cool in the tin.

Separate the egg whites from the yolks. Place the rest of the ingredients, together with the egg yolks, into a large mixing bowl and beat well. Whisk the egg whites until they form stiff peaks. Then, using a metal spoon, carefully fold into the cheese batter. Spoon the mixture into the pastry case, levelling the surface.

Bake for 30–35 minutes until set. Transfer to a wire rack and leave to cool.

Remove the side of the tin and use a metal spatula to transfer the cake to a serving plate.

PEACH TART
For the pastry

1 cup rice flour

1 cup cornmeal

½ cup butter

25 gm unrefined caster sugar

1 large organic egg yolk

For the filling

½ cup unrefined caster sugar

½ cup butter

1 organic egg, beaten

1/3rd cup ground rice / rice flour

½ cup ground almonds

A few drops natural almond essence

3–4 peaches, stoned, poached and sliced

A little organic icing sugar for dusting (optional)

Halve the peaches to remove the stones. Place in a shallow fry pan skin side down, cover with cold water, bring to the boil and poach for 10–15 minutes. Using a slotted spoon, remove the cooked fruit onto a plate; cool slightly then remove the skin with the point of a sharp knife. It should lift off easily. Slice the peach halves evenly into 4 or 6 portions, as desired, down the north-south polarity.

Mix the cornmeal and rice flour together in a large mixing bowl. Lightly rub in the butter until the mixture resembles fine breadcrumbs. Add the sugar, stir in the egg yolk and add sufficient chilled water to obtain a soft, but not sticky, dough. Wrap this in cling film and chill for ½ hour.

Heat the oven (Gas 4 / 180 C).

In a mixing bowl cream the butter and sugar until the mixture is light and fluffy, and then gradually add the egg, beating well until thoroughly blended. Fold in the ground rice and ground almonds along with the almond essence.

With light fingers, line a 24 cm loose-bottomed flan tin with the pastry by pressing it into the base and up the sides, and ensure there are no holes. Spoon the almond mixture into the pastry case. Arrange the cold sliced peaches on top. Any slices left over, retain for decoration.

Place the flan tin on a baking sheet and bake for 40–45 minutes until both filling and pastry are cooked and lightly browned.

Serve warm or cold dusted with icing sugar. If you have any peach slices left over, arrange on top. Crème fraîche goes very well with this tart.

Variation
Substitute fresh apricots for peaches in season. You will require 10–12. There is no need to poach the apricots because you do not remove the skin. Simply halve and remove the pits.

NEW ZEALAND MOIST CARROT CAKE

For the Cake

9 oz wholemeal flour

6 oz raw cane sugar (Muscovado)

6 oz soft brown sugar

3 tbs raisins or sultanas

3 standard sized organic eggs

6 fl.oz organic sunflower oil

2 fl.oz soured cream

3 oz. desiccated coconut

1 tsp freshly ground nutmeg

½ tsp ground ginger

2 level tsp cinnamon

1 tsp bicarbonate of soda

½ tsp sea salt

11 oz grated carrots

2 tsp pure vanilla essence

For the topping

4 oz full fat soft cream cheese

2 oz unsalted butter

2 oz sifted icing sugar

Juice of ½ lemon

The most delicious carrot cake I have ever tasted!

Anne Dawson enticed me with a piece of this cake at a fund-raising jazz evening and was kind enough to donate her recipe.

Pre-heat the oven (Gas 3 / 150 C)

Line an 8" round cake tine with baking parchment.

Use 2 mixing bowls.

In the first bowl place the eggs, oil, vanilla essence and soured cream. Sieve in the sugars (to avoid lumps). Beat to a smooth consistency.

In the second bowl sift the flour, nutmeg, cinnamon, ginger, bicarbonate of soda and salt. Then pour in the wet ingredients, beating well. Add the carrots, coconut, raisins / sultanas and mix well to ensure even distribution of ingredients. Spoon into the cake tin, and bake in the centre of the oven for 1½–2 hours.

When the cake is cool, mix the topping ingredients together and spread thickly over the top.

SECTION SEVEN

FRAGMENTED, PARTIAL, SYNTHETIC and WHOLEFOODS

Milk, Sugar, Fats and Supplements

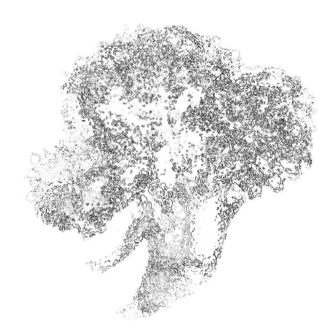

Science, particularly medical and food science, has developed rapidly during my lifetime. It is now possible for damaged body parts to be transplanted or grown from stem cells. Naturally occurring substances can be replicated in a laboratory and deficiencies in diet supplemented artificially. Human beings are increasingly being treated like cars – worn out parts are replaced at the garage (hospital) so that the lifespan of the vehicle (person) can be extended and, as a result, we are in danger of losing sight of some basic truths.

As living entities humans are designed to function as a system. That is to say we are a collection of identifiable separate parts which individually interact to operate as a whole. Each part is dependent upon the other parts to one degree or another to keep the whole organism operational, balanced and wholesome. Some parts such as the brain, heart, lungs, liver, and kidneys have a more fundamental role than do others in maintaining continuity of life. Where lesser parts become impaired or dysfunctional, the whole system will reorganise itself towards re-balance in order to function as a whole entity once more. Loss of the major organs usually means loss of life unless there is a possibility of technological intervention such as a transplant, whereas the loss of a limb may impair function but it is not usually lethal. External pathogens that threaten the organism will be met with resistance locally and then, if necessary, by the whole organism functioning as a single unit. Any healthy body – plant or animal – is designed and equipped to repel invaders.

What is true for us is true for all living entities and this is what differentiates them from things which are non-living entities. A car or computer is also a collection of parts which, when operated by a human, functions as a unit. But without the human component – i.e. when the machine is switched off – it reverts to being just a collection of parts that can be taken out, put back in, replaced or repaired without impacting on any other. A switched-off machine is helpless.

A machine has a pre-determined role and life span and from the moment it comes off the production line it is subject to the physical processes of decay without any means of self-renewal. The individual components of a car are similar in design and function to those of a ship or an aeroplane. But once assembled as a car they can never develop into any of the other means of transport. All beings share a basic set of components but these are designed and programmed by Nature to develop in myriad ways from a single cell and fulfil a potential.

Human beings, to date the most complicated design on the planet, come "out of production" into the world as babies and, hopefully, will grow and mature into adults. And when we have completed the physical cycle of growth there is all the inner development still working as a continuum towards self-awareness or consciousness. In other words, beings for their entire lifespan are in a constant state of becoming. We are designed to create and make choices, continuously, for better or worse. We learn from our experiences, we communicate feelings, ideas and experience, and we socialise.

As a composite of intelligent interacting parts, we are individual components within larger systems: we are part of a family, a community, and a nation and so on. As individuals we are constantly interacting with everything that is not us, and it is these interactions that impact upon the quality of our individual life.

It is important, therefore, we always remember the bigger picture when dealing with a living organism as it is constantly in a state of flux compared to a machine. What we do to one part of the entity will have consequences for other parts. This is as true for what we feed it as for all other interventions.

WHOLEFOODS, PARTIAL FOODS AND FRAGMENTED FOODS

Hunters and gatherers ate what they could find. So the human body is designed to digest and utilise all that it eats to support all its functions – not just physical but spiritual and social as well. Our first food is human milk, a wholefood which combines protein, fat and carbohydrates (as well as minerals) in a specific ratio where the carbohydrate content is more than double the fat content and almost ten times the protein content.

Anne-Marie Colbin postulates that, when weaned, the human organism will continue to seek its nutrients proportionately. That is to say, if the main component of a meal is a piece of meat (concentrated protein and possibly fat) then the body will instinctively seek some concentrated carbohydrate such as potato or a sweet dessert (flour and sugar) to balance it. Similarly, if we eat cheese (fat and protein) we often accompany it with bread or biscuits (carbohydrate). Such balances are obtained arbitrarily, determined by the amount of specific concentrations, and the implication is that a diet obtained mostly from concentrated, partial foods can place a strain on the organism that results ultimately in a breakdown in our own health.

In other words, the incessant ingestion of partial or fragmented foods is mirrored in us: our wholesomeness becomes fragmented.

A wholefood is one which is proportionately balanced by Nature from the outset so where the diet comprises mostly whole grains and fresh vegetables the violent swings between the different concentrations will decrease. As outlined above, humans are more than their physical system; they are their mental, emotional and spiritual dimensions as well. Food does not just impact on us physically, it affects our emotions. If our diet comprises mostly stressed (de-natured foods) it will affect our mood swings adversely.

In my late twenties and early thirties I suffered from PMT which worsened progressively. I tried standard self-help supplements from B6 to evening primrose oil and I resorted to homeopathy. All to little avail and the consternation of my long-suffering spouse, who was on the receiving end of these irrational mood swings. Then, for an altogether unrelated reason, I changed my meat-based diet to a vegetarian one and the symptoms vanished overnight. That is not to advocate vegetarianism per se as a "cure" for PMT; it was a solution for me.

Looking back I remembered that the onset of my PMT coincided with going to live in New Zealand where meat featured much more heavily in the national diet than it did in the UK. Meat, particularly sheep meat, was both cheap and abundant; it was the norm to buy a side of mutton as opposed to two chops. The problem was not the meat; it was the amount I was consuming that threw my whole system out of balance. And when my hormones were in a state of flux this proportional imbalance in my diet rendered me vicious.

I am not recommending abstinence from any particular food; I am simply trying to raise some awareness about dietary habits by suggesting that it is what we do most that determines the overall health of our being. An occasional binge on chips and chocolate is not going to cause harm in the long run, but a nightly indulgence will make an impact.

The nearest we come to consuming the wholefood is when we eat nuts, seeds, whole grains and legumes. These foods are the product of the plant, containing energetically all the vital ingredients for the regeneration of a particular species from a hazelnut tree to a pea. Other vegetables and fruit (particularly when we eat the skins and pips) come a very close second to the former.

Refined or fragmented foods are a step further away from whole foods. The processed food industry developed out of a necessity to supply an ever-increasing world population with essential nourishment that it could no longer obtain from its own labours. Frozen lamb from New Zealand fed Britain's burgeoning city populations whilst tinned baked beans fed America's cowboys on the range. What "goodness" was lost in the process was compensated by removing the choice between living and dying! Cowboys would resume a more balanced diet on returning to town and in Britain cooked frozen meat was eaten with fresh vegetables.

From these early beginnings and well-meaning intentions, however, the processed foods industry has harnessed science to manipulate foods not only beyond all recognition but also beyond their ability to achieve their original purpose – nourish a human being to fulfil its potential.

A refined foodstuff is one where most of the essential elements have been stripped out leaving a highly concentrated residue. Refined grains, sold as flours, are mostly carbohydrate devoid of fibre and essential minerals. In accordance with Ms. Colbin's philosophy, highly concentrated protein foods such as meat or dairy will seek an extreme form of carbohydrate: ice cream, chocolate mousse, (high white sugar content); sticky toffee pudding (white flour, white sugar) for compensation. However, a meal that combines meat with whole grains such as brown rice will feel more satisfying and a sweet course may be rendered minimal or optional.[1]

Food manufacturers, not content with refining grains into flours of little nutritional value, have given us grains processed as breakfast cereal. Cornflakes, bran flakes, puffed rice etc. are cereals rendered unrecognisable from their natural state, heavily laced with sugar and salt to make them palatable and, to crown the feast, fortified with artificial vitamins. "Putting back something that has been removed does not equate with leaving it in to begin with" [2], because the life force of the nutrient will have been invalidated.

Such foods may sustain us for a time on the gross physical level, but the subtler aspects of our being will not be optimally nourished, if at all. Subtle energies interact with subtle energies. A dead "food" has no subtle energy, only a collection of physical components. When we are hungry, statements like "I'm famished" or "I'm dying to eat" may be more literal than we realise.

We need expansive (build-up) and contractive (breakdown) foods that will balance in a good diet. In the west there is a tendency to consume too much build-up food at the expense of breakdown foods.

But within that generalisation there are variables: children require more build-up foods than adults; physically active people will require more build-up foods than those leading a predominantly sedentary lifestyle. We need to balance the acid-alkaline intake: meat, dairy, fish, grains and legumes are acid forming foods, whereas fruit and vegetables alkalise. In general we consume too much of the former at the expense of the latter, which is why we are currently being exhorted to eat more fruit and vegetables. If that sounds too complicated, a good rule of thumb is to ensure that our diet leans mostly towards fresh vegetables and fruit, with the emphasis on vegetables.

A proportionately balanced diet based on the above guideline could look something like this:–

Designer diets are based on standardisation. They either: forbid specific foods, deal in weights and measures, or supplement, which is why they rarely "work" long term and are often difficult to complete. Colbin's book *"Food and Healing"* combines intuitive wisdom with scientific rationale and suggests that as a whole system we are best served nutritionally by whole foods (which are also living systems), rather than fragmented foods (destroyed systems), or synthetic foods: artificial supplements and food substitutes such as sweeteners (standardised systems). [3]

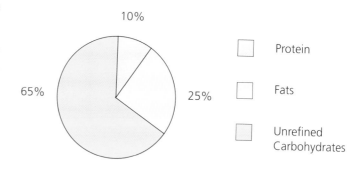

In yoga the Breath serves as a metaphor for Life in all its myriad dimensions and context. The basic rhythm of the breath demonstrates the primal rhythm of our Universe: expansion (inhalation), pause, and contraction (exhalation). Bear in mind we live this rhythm from our first inhalation to our final exhalation. In between the two is our lifespan and food is its major support system. For optimum health it pays to be aware of its rhythms – the point at which it is most nourishing – as well as its physical properties.

[1] Colbin op.cit

[2] Colbin ibid.

[3] Colbin apart, the rationale behind the intrinsic of foods is perhaps best explained by Rudolph Hauschka in his works *"Nutrition"* and *"The Nature of Substance"*, and by Rudolph Ballantine M.D. *"Diet and Nutrition (a holistic approach)"*. All these books are written in terms that can be readily grasped by the lay person.

Cows' milk in its raw state, unlike sugar and fats which are concentrates, is a wholefood (for calves). All three are nourishing foods in their own right when used moderately, in amounts that cannot be pre-determined other than by the individual. Because milk is usually taken as a liquid there is a tendency to think of it as a drink rather than a food, and drinking it ensures that we take in more than we actually need. Most health problems with all three foods derive from taking them to excess.

Our bodies, constantly striving for balance, seek to expel anything surplus to requirements and when the organs of elimination (skin, lungs, liver, kidneys and intestines) are working efficiently there is no problem. Where any inefficiency or malfunction develops amongst these organs, what cannot be expelled is stored in the body tissues until such time as the body can deal with it, which is sometimes never and the consequences can be unfortunate.

It is reminiscent of the unexpected phone call from a house-proud relative or friend announcing an imminent arrival. Panic sets in and there is a rush to tidy up so as not to offend their sensibilities. Everything out of place gets shoved out of sight, behind cushions, into cupboards, behind large pieces of furniture, under chairs with a mental promise to clear them away properly after the visit. But we are so busy and after the visitor's departure something else requires our attention. The children need picking up, it is time to shop, prepare the dinner, make notes for tomorrow's meeting, meet a deadline and so on and so forth. Then before we know it, someone else is going to call, and there is another mess to clear up. Eventually the cupboards burst open and everything that should not have been put there in the first places tumbles out.

Many chronic health problems in the West emanate from a disproportionate intake of building foods

such as milk and dairy products. Milk may not of itself cause a problem whereas taking it daily on breakfast cereal, (more building food) and as a matter of routine (every time we have a cup of coffee or tea) might. Asthma, allergies, ear infections, sinusitis, strep throat, tonsillitis, acne and excessive weight gain are amongst the most common symptoms associated with excess intake of these foods and inefficient excretion. Many people suffering from these complaints find their symptoms disappear and experience a rise in energy levels, once they stop using dairy products as a main source of food. Including plenty of breakdown foods (fresh fruit and vegetables) as a counterbalance to the dairy could alleviate or resolve problems associated with dairy for some people.

For my generation downing the government-funded $^{1}/_{3}$rd pint school milk was a daily ritual, as obligatory as morning prayers. Supplying milk to children was a sincere attempt on the part of material science to ensure we did not develop rickets, the vitamin D calcium-linked deficiency disease that haunted my great- grandparents' generation. This automatic provision of "free school milk" was abolished in the 1970s in the interests of economy and the stated belief that overall nutrition had improved to such an extent, public funded milk was superfluous and unwarranted.

Milk is regarded as the original substance of life. Whether this first food continues to be ideal beyond weaning is debatable and controversial. Only humans continue to ingest milk (from other mammals) after being weaned. Animals stop producing the enzyme needed to digest their infant food on weaning.

Colbin suggests that some people –for whom milk is a staple–(nomads and vegetarian Hindus for instance) have developed the genetic ability to continue producing the enzyme, lactase, and can digest milk throughout their adult lives but the rest of us has lost that ability to some extent and she claims 25% of the Caucasian population in the USA is allergic to lactose (milk sugar).[4] Ballantine, however, would appear to dispute this. He claims any peoples descended from an ancestry where dairying has been practised for many centuries will continue to tolerate milk beyond weaning and, in specific reference to the white American population, states "….only 6 to 15% of them will show symptoms of milk (lactose) intolerance". It is in those ethnic groups where drinking milk beyond weaning is not traditional that problems of intolerance arise.[5]

Drinking pasteurised milk can lead to severe constipation. In its raw form milk is a reasonable source of protein but the availability of unpasteurised green top milk was outlawed in the late 1990s. Irrespective of the arguments about bacteria and TB, pasteurising milk ensures the loss of 10% of the B vitamins and 50% vitamin C. More importantly, the pasteurisation process alters milk in such a way it breaks the complex protein chain so that the molecules collapse in a tangled heap, and the digestive enzymes experience difficulty separating and metabolising the amino acids.[6]

There also appears to be a relationship between colic in breast-fed babies and the pasteurised cows' milk drunk by their mothers. And it may be a direct or indirect factor in infant dermatitis, which is another condition that appears to be on the increase. If breast milk is not available for the baby, goats' milk is the next best choice since it appears to produce fewer allergic reactions than cows' milk.

After weaning, I fed my children raw, organic milk in New Zealand and the equivalent green top milk in the UK whilst it was possible to do so. I also used fresh unpasteurised goats' milk successfully with one of the children for whom cows' milk proved unsuitable. Academic arguments aside, I found the taste of raw, unpasteurised milk infinitely preferable to the pasteurised / homogenised product we use today.

And I am convinced I am not alone. When I lived on Tyneside, milk on the doorstep would occasionally be appropriated by revellers returning home in the small hours. This could prove a nuisance for any busy household inasmuch as it required an unscheduled walk to the local shop before breakfast. For me, who refused to entertain the idea of giving the children pasteurised milk as an alternative, the theft went beyond mere inconvenience. Obviously the freeloaders became as convinced as I was of the superiority of raw milk because my doorstep became the preferred port of call over my neighbours'.

Country folklore has it that a cow with a calf is potentially more dangerous than a bull, and the human animal is no exception. Paranoia helped develop a sort of sixth sense in me as to when the milk would be taken. This resulted one night in an irate, night-attired mother, shrieking like a banshee, chasing two spindle-legged youths up a (thankfully) deserted road. Terror, plus the fact that I was barefoot, lent them the required speed to ensure a successful get away.

Strangely, Northumbria police were not impressed when I suggested our street required the services of a regular officer on patrol. My remedy, a concoction of near-lethal natural laxatives, brewed up to look like milk and placed strategically on the doorstep before retiring, had my husband looking up to see whether the witchcraft laws had been repealed and the children wanting to know whether I would be carted off to prison. An asylum for the unhinged more likely was their father's caustic retort.

Fortunate perhaps, the night-callers did not avail themselves of a brew designed to exact a natural justice swifter than the time taken to unzip a pair of drainpipe jeans. Not that they would have drunk it – one sniff would have alerted even the most inebriated to the fact that it was not milk! The practical solution was to ask the farm to supply me through my wholefood shop which co-incidentally ensured others developed a taste for it. Until it was banned. Nowadays, when I want to use milk, although I have no option but to use pasteurised, I ensure it is at least organic.

Colbin links dairy produce to various disorders of the female reproductive system, some serious, others less so, and cites reversals occurring simply through eliminating dairy from the diet. She has found women appear to suffer more than men from the build-up, blocking effects of milk, which makes sense from a systems point of view because milk is supposed to flow out of, not into, women.[7]

My husband enjoys milk and cream to a degree I am unable to tolerate, and dairy plays a considerable part in his diet. Nowadays I use dairy sparingly. For personal use I substitute Soya for cows' milk though, when I am out with friends, I will happily drink a cappuccino or partake of dairy-based foods, because I do not suffer from intolerance. For those who do, there are several alternatives such as soya, rice and oat milk. These can be successfully substituted for cows' milk in most of the recipes in the book.

Nowadays the practice is to homogenise pasteurised milk so that the cream remains blended instead of rising to the top. Homogenisation breaks up the milk molecules into smaller pieces but some of these substances pass through the intestinal wall unaltered by the digestive process. One of these, xanthine oxydase, after passing through the intestinal wall and being picked up by the lymphatic system, travels through the arteries scratching the inside of the arterial walls, and causing small primary lesions. As a defence against this the body deposits fibrin and cholesterol over the lesions to prevent further damage.[8]

Skimmed milk is designed to reduce our fat intake and save our hearts. Yet human milk has a relatively higher fat content than cow's milk. Butterfat contains a protein-splitting enzyme, so if we remove the butterfat we have difficulty digesting milk protein; and we require the butterfat if we want to utilise the calcium. Which just goes to prove, again, the more we tamper with the food supply, the more we fragment it, analyse it and argue over the benefits of single nutrients, the less nutritious we render it.

Amongst other substances in daily use, we are constantly being urged to lower our salt intake. Human milk contains about $1/3^{rd}$ the amount of sodium found in cow's milk yet salt is added to cows' milk cheeses to enhance flavour. Cows' milk along with cheese could be amongst the most common sources of excess sodium in the standard British diet.

Despite this I still eat cheese and for preference I buy mostly locally produced Northumbrian cheese, and other unpasteurised varieties. Northumbrian sheep cheese is particularly delicious and a tiny portion goes a long way. Yoghurt and fermented milk such as buttermilk are easier foods for us to assimilate because the lactose has been broken down during the fermentation process.

Milk from other mammals has a different chemical composition and energy field from human milk. According to Colbin, if we put 100 gm cows' milk into the human system we obtain 2.4 gm protein, and 85 mg calcium more than it needs.[9] This apart, milk and dairy contain useful nutrients and for some peoples raw milk is a staple food. In our culture, where our nutritional needs are being met from other sources milk will be superfluous to our requirements and it may be sensible to abandon using it if health problems develop.

And, interestingly, from an esoteric perspective, Colbin suggests that if we continue to ingest a food designed for infants we will be suspended in a child-like state, dependent, and unable to fulfil our potential.[10] (Section Ten)

[4] Colbin op.cit. p 156

[5] Ballantine op.cit. pp126-128

[6] Ibid p 128

[7] Colbin op.cit p 153

[8] Colbin op.cit pp 154-155

[9] Anne-Marie Colbin *Food and Healing* pp 148-157

[10] Ibid. p 157

SUGAR

Chinese philosophy holds that for nutritional satisfaction we need a balance of 5 tastes: sweet, salty, astringent (sharp), sour and bitter. A predilection for sweet food is innate, going back to when we were hunter-gatherers and we learned the sweeter the berry the less likely our chances of being poisoned. Nowadays the reverse probably holds true because we consume sugar and salt almost to the exclusion of the other three tastes, and in particular the bitter one. I have wondered whether our predilection for chocolate is less a craving for sugar than a desire for the bitter taste otherwise absent from most peoples' diet. Cocoa is naturally bitter and was originally taken unsweetened.

When sugar was first introduced to Europe it was used very sparingly. With large scale production of cane sugar and the manipulation of beets into sugar during the late eighteenth century, the product became readily available to the masses but as the adage goes " a little of something that is good for you, does not mean a lot of it is better".

Understanding the adverse effects of sugar on the human system does not prevent us from finding it attractive. An East African childhood ensured I attended boarding school from age seven and a singular delight was the privilege of food parcels from home. These food parcels, by popular request, contained copious quantities of condensed milk without which no midnight feast would have been worthy of the name. Although I can no longer stomach condensed milk, I still recall all the pleasurable sensations associated with an index finger exploring the inside rim of the tin, slowly scooping out the thick, sticky goo, sucking it and following it all the way down from throat to stomach. Greedy little beasts that we were, such practice invariably ensured we were sick. Or it may have been the tinned pilchards that followed! Food parcels apart, I should add sweets were not the daily occurrence they are nowadays but a Saturday treat to accompany the weekly film show.

The 1939-45 British wartime diet is sometimes extolled in comparison with the standard diet in place today. The former was low in butter, eggs and sugar and when rationing was abolished adults delighted in offering to children what they had denied themselves during a long period of national restraint. During childhood visits to England aunts and uncles indulged me with chocolate, ice cream and sweeties. I suggest such practice, meant originally as a kindness, has developed into a daily expectation for many people. Added to which we have sweetened flavoured milk and crisps.

Government figures suggest that average sucrose consumption had risen as high as 38kg per head per annum by the late 1980s. This could be an understatement: my unofficial sampling of teenagers during their school lunch break, over a period of six months in 1989, would average at least 45kg per child per annum, and that estimate is conservative. Excess sugar has been blamed for rotting teeth and a rise in diabetes but this picture is only partial because of our fragmentary approach to health care. Little, if any, connection is made with decaying teeth in childhood, diabetes in the teens, arthritis in adulthood and osteoporosis in later life.

Processed foods are laced with sugar and I used to suggest to students that one way of finding out how much sugar they were consuming was to look at the labelling for the percentage of sugar used in all the processed foods they consumed over one week. For cooking and home-baking, and for every spoonful added to tea, coffee or cereal, they had to put an equivalent amount in a jar. Most were astonished by their findings.

Although many of these problems will have existed prior to easy access to sugar, on a mental and emotional level a link has been established between sugar consumption and hyperactivity in children, lack of concentration, depression, anxiety, psychological disorders, insanity and violent criminal behaviour. Suicide is often an outcome of depression and in this country the suicide rate is rising.

Macrobiotic practitioners in the USA, after being allowed to implement dietary reforms in certain penal institutions, claimed an 85% reduction in disruptive behaviour amongst inmates.[11] Alexander Schauss would place that figure much higher: he suggests 95% of criminal behaviour can be linked to fragmentary dietary habits (a junk diet).[12]

Whilst it is simplistic to place blame for anti-social behaviour on sugar alone, it would be foolish to dismiss the sugar factor altogether. Many people living on fragmented sub-standard diets obtain their calories from cheap, sugared foods and drinks. It is possible that a considerable proportion of social problems, including crime, are directly related to the malnourished and demineralised condition of individuals who exist largely on these foods.

However, neither suppressing the desire for sugar, nor substituting it with artificial sweeteners, all of which are suspect from a health point of view, is a rational reaction whereas an understanding of the nature of sugar and how we interact with it allows for real choice as to how much, if any, we continue to consume.

We have all been introduced to sugar at birth. Human milk contains sugar in the form of lactose and proportionately yields twice the amount of milk sugar as cows' milk[13], which possibly explains the popularity of adding sucrose to cow's milk when this is used as a substitute for infant feed. Milk and biscuits are often paired for snacks.

Sucrose is a refined product obtained from cane and beet sugar. In Nature sugars (refined carbohydrate) are converted naturally from starch (unrefined carbohydrate) by the sun's action. We imitate this activity by applying heat to substance but in the manufacturing process we lose a lot of what Nature leaves intact. Cane sugar is obtained by stripping out the minerals and fibre, leaving a liquid carbohydrate residue that is heated until it crystallises into the pure white elemental form we call sugar.

One East African township where we lived housed a sugar refinery and, depending on the wind direction, the air was often sweetly fragrant. The smell of sugar was augmented to a cloying degree by the practice of spraying the tacky by-product on the local roads to keep dust levels down. This thick, treacle-brown residue was the rich molasses that contained all the natural goodness of the sugar cane and we were literally throwing it away. Dark, soft brown sugar, sold as Barbados or Muscovado sugar, is rich in nutrients and can be utilised in place of white sugar in many recipes, including some cakes. For sponges I substitute natural cane caster sugars for white, and I use natural cane sugars or Demerara wherever Muscovado would be inappropriate.

All sugar is acid forming to a degree and, in order to neutralise the corrosive effects of acids, we require an alkali for balance. Minerals alkalise and are stored in the body, mostly in the bones. When we ingest a sugar depleted of its mineral content (white sugar) our body has to rely entirely on its own reserves in order to process it. These reserves vary individually depending on the whole diet and the individual's predisposition to absorbing nutrients from the food supply. If we demineralise our system in processing the sugar-intake we become weakened and predisposed to chronic and crippling diseases, many of which may not advertise themselves until we are advanced in years, by which time they may be irreversible.

For example, by raising the insulin level, sugar inhibits the release of growth hormones, a situation that in turn depresses the immune system and today we are witnessing an increase in the so-called auto-immune diseases, as well as heart disease and diabetes.

Problems arise when the sugar intake provides more naked carbohydrate than is required to balance the protein intake. Since white flour also supplies naked carbohydrate it is possible that very small amounts of white sugar will create excess. During the last 3 decades there has been an increasing interest in vegetarianism but continuing to eat white sugar after abandoning meat is ill advised: from a macrobiotic stand point, meat (concentrated fat and protein) dovetails perfectly with sugar (concentrated carbohydrate). The one is an extreme yang food, the other extreme yin so they balance.

I have facetiously claimed to friends that my husband ingests enough natural cane sugar to fell an elephant which possibly explains why he also likes to eat meat daily. The fact that in over thirty years, this even-tempered, personable individual has never needed the ministrations of a doctor suggests he is eating a diet balanced for his needs. I should perhaps stress that his diet also includes a large proportion of vegetables and fruit. A vegetarian diet that is disproportionately high in white sugar will unbalance the protein: carbohydrate ratio and has been linked to learning difficulties and behavioural disorders.[14]

Rudolph Hauschka explains that on a mental dimension cane sugar's function strengthens ego awareness and enhances personality. We speak of sweet-natured personalities, and also of sugary dispositions! If someone is kind we associate the kindness with sweetness and we are drawn towards sweet people as surely as bees are drawn to nectar and bears to honey.

On a mental plane beet sugar affects us quite differently from cane sugar. Under a microscope sugar crystals, whether from cane or beets, will look the same but their function is entirely different. Cane sugar is the product of the plant stem and, therefore, interacts with our rhythmic system and nourishes the warmth of the being. Beet sugar, deriving from a root, interacts with the human head polarity, which is cold. It stimulates the intellect, which in the west is already over-exercised at the expense of our feelings and metabolism. Sugar serves us best as a warming food, not a cold one. Hauschka believes it is no coincidence that refined white sugar (from beets) was made

available to us in any significant quantity at that period in our history known as The Age of Reason. [15]

Currently we are entering a new phase of development: a greater consciousness of our environment in relation to ourselves is almost universal. Hauschka maintains that sugar has completed its task when people have developed a full consciousness of themselves as individuals and of their place within the universal order. After that stage of development even small quantities become superfluous. If sugar as food has served its purpose cosmically and our intelligence is urging its abandonment we would be wise to heed it. Otherwise we become sick.

As for sugar substitutes – almost universal in sugar-free products– I would not consider putting such substances in my body. In 1981 a book called *Cover Up: The facts they don't want you to know"* (sadly now out of print), Nicholas Hildyard exposed the lengths that manufacturer Searle went to get their artificial sweetener accepted by the American Food and Drug Agency. I cannot help but wonder how much of the Nation's obsession with sweetness and salt, at the expense of the sour sharp and bitter tastes has led to imbalance and obesity.

[11] *Crime and Diet*: Michio Kushi

[12] *Crime, Delinquency and Diet:* Alexander Schauss

[13] Anne-Marie Colbin op.cit. p 151

[14] Colbin op.cit. p119

[15] For a full treatise on this subject read Rudolph Hauschka's *"Nature of Substance"* and *"Nutrition"*

Some alternatives to sugar

Pear and apple spread

Date, rice, maple syrups

Sugar-free jams and marmalade

Honey

Sweeteners for stewed fruit

Dates, raisins, sultanas, figs

Rice syrup

Barley malt

Concentrated fruit juices: apple, blackcurrant, pear

**Sugar-free drinks
without artificial sweeteners**

There are many branded varieties available in both health food outlets and supermarkets. My children used to claim Suma's orange concentrate combined with Perrier water "tastes just like Fanta".

FRUIT SPONGE CAKE

6 oz butter

6 oz chopped dates stewed to a pulp in a little water

6 oz wholewheat flour

1 heaped tsp baking powder

3 oz mixed dried fruit

3 large organic eggs well beaten

½ grated apple

1 large tsp, cinnamon

Grease and line a 2 lb loaf tin. Cream the dates and butter, add the flour, spice, eggs and baking powder, mixing thoroughly, then add the mixed fruit and grated apple. Bake in the centre of a pre-heated oven (Gas 4 / 180 C) for 40-50 minutes. Allow to cool slightly before turning out.

FATS

Despite the fashion for low-fat or fat-free foods, we need fats in our diet for lubrication and for warmth. Optimum amounts vary from one individual to another, which is rather like determining the length of the proverbial piece of string but as always with concentrates, the emphasis needs to be on moderation. Where fat is used as a spread it should be as an accompaniment to the bread / toast / biscuit not the other way about and fried foods should be minimal.

I have always used fats liberally, without any ill effects so far, whereas I exercise caution with sugar. I use organic butter as a spread and never replace it with margarine or vegetable substitutes. For cooking I use mostly ghee and organic cold-pressed oils, although I generally add oils to food in preference to cooking with them as heating can damage their delicate structures. Oil will lift a salad.

It also enriches steamed vegetables, as does butter. I adopt this practice more often during the colder months than in the summer. Notwithstanding global warming or central heating, our winters are decidedly chilly to the point of freezing and I cannot imagine anything less appetising than a white, steamed parsnip when icy rain is lashing against the windows. Enriching vegetables with butter or oils is also a foolproof way of getting some heat into scantily clad, vegetarian, teenage girls hell-bent on a night out in defiance of the elements. I was fortunate that my daughter's favourite vegetable is potato – mashed potato is a wonderful vehicle for butter or cream.

An ideal source of fats is nuts and seeds because they are wholefoods. Once upon a time, in more rural and labour-intensive communities, hand-grinding nuts and seeds specifically for a purpose ensured regular fresh supplies of oils. Such practice is inappropriate for the majority of westerners living in sophisticated technological societies and, besides, nuts and seeds are often regarded as fattening without necessarily being considered a desirable source of fat. Instead they are commonly associated with snack foods, ingredients added to muesli, confectionery or vegetarian meat substitutes.

Nuts and seeds apart, fat consumption is a contentious issue linked to heart disease and, specifically, arteriosclerosis. Current medical opinion favours polyunsaturated as opposed to saturated fats but the preference is misleading. If overall fat consumption is disproportionately high in relation to other nutrients and if the diet comprises mainly fragmented (junk) foods, it matters less whether the fat intake is saturated or unsaturated than that the diet is already unwholesome: a predisposition to disease exists.

To make rational choices about fat consumption it is useful to know what fats are, what differentiates a saturated fat from an unsaturated one, and how we process them.

Fats are hydrocarbon chains structurally related to petroleum. Each carbon atom has the space to attach to 4 other atoms. When all these spaces are taken up by hydrogen atoms the fat is said to be saturated. As a rule of thumb, fats solid at room temperature are said to be saturated whereas liquids are unsaturated. But that is not the whole story since some saturated fats are held to be more saturated than others, the degree of saturation being determined by the length of the carbon chains and the melting point of the fat. The longer the carbon chain the more solid the fat. Butterfat chains are shorter than beef fat chains so butter is considered a less saturated fat than beef fat because, at room temperature, butter will soften whereas beef tallow remains solid enough to be used in candle-making.

We require cholesterol for fat digestion. Our bodies naturally produce cholesterol for this very purpose. It is a waxy fat-like substance that is the base from which oestrogen, cortisone and testosterone are made. It is also a component of nerve tissue. One end of the molecule forms a salt soluble in water and the other end combines readily with fat. This allows cholesterol (or bile salts) to promote the mixture of fats in the small intestine with water so they can be broken down for absorption through the intestinal wall.

Cholesterol can cause trouble if it accumulates as a plaque along blood vessel walls and nothing is done to halt the process. If these deposits thicken to narrow the walls arteriosclerosis is the result, manifesting as leg pains, breathlessness, angina and stroke.

Cholesterol-related problems are not caused by the production of cholesterol in itself but from the consumption of fragmented, fibre-depleted foodstuffs like white flour and white sugar. Where the diet is nutritionally balanced – high in fibre from whole grains, beans, fruits and fresh vegetables – there should be no problems associated with cholesterol because any excess will be mopped up by the roughage and safely eliminated via the large intestine. Oats are a particularly effective agent for dealing with this hazardous waste because it adheres to their gummy fibres prior to expulsion. And data exists which suggests buttermilk, unlike other animal fats, actually has a protective effect on the heart[16]

Should you develop arteriosclerosis, Rudolph Ballantine MD maintains that it can be reversed provided the diet is altered to one low in sugars, high in vegetables, rich in minerals and vitamins and very low in fat. Oils have to be consumed only as nuts and seeds; cooking and salad oils are prohibited. He allows for occasional very small amounts of butterfat, stressing that the total intake of fat from all sources be limited to between 10–15% of the calorific intake, which means the virtual elimination of all meat. This, of course, is crisis management.

Since 1977 Dr. Dean Ornish, another American, has been developing a drug-free, non-surgical intervention programme for people with documented coronary heart disease. This programme, a combination of remedial diet, stress-management and yoga, has led to significant improvements for the majority of people suffering heart disease who have undertaken it for one year.

Nowadays we are used to lean meat but even these cuts can contain up to 50% fat. The amount of fat in meat is less important than the type of fat laid down by the animal. A free-ranging animal will lay down unsaturated fat to saturated fat in the ratio of 3:1, whereas in an intensively reared one this proportion is reversed and it is the saturated fat that demands caution.[17]

Another controversial subject is margarine – alleged to be better for us than butter. Compared with the length of time humans have been ingesting butter, margarine is a novelty food. The invention of a Frenchman during the late nineteenth century Franco-Prussian siege of Paris, margarine was made palatable in this country during the last World War when butter had to be strictly rationed. It was not a popular substitute at the time and, though improvements have been made to its flavour so that some people have come to prefer its taste to that of butter, its acceptability today is possibly due to a belief in its so-called health properties.

"High in polyunsaturates" is a slogan favoured by margarine manufacturers, based no doubt on the vegetable origins of the ingredients. That the end product is solid at room temperature means it is saturated, artificially, by a process known as hydrogenation. According to Dr. Ballantine, writing in the 1970s, "where margarine and vegetable shortening is widely used in England the rate of heart disease has been found to be higher than in those areas where it is not used." He went on to state "in the South eastern states of America, the region where margarine consumption is highest in relation to the population and butter consumption, the incidence of heart disease is sufficiently high as to be termed an enigma". He concludes that margarine, instead of preventing heart attacks, actually accelerates the process causing them.[18]

None of the recipes in this book advocates the use of margarine although for those who are convinced of its virtues, the butter quantities can be substituted with their preferred alternative.

The efficacy of vegetable oils is also questionable. Heart disease decreased in studies where people changed to vegetable oils but the mortality rate did not fall. As heart disease rates went down the cancer rate went up and where patients showed an unusual frequency of malignant melanoma (a rapid, often fatal, form of skin cancer) further enquiry into their dietary habits showed that there had recently been an enthusiastic switch from butter to oils.[19] We are warned persistently about the dangers of developing skin cancer from over- exposure to the sun's harmful rays but a depleted ozone layer may not by itself be responsible for an increasing number of people developing this condition. Could there be a relationship between an increased consumption of polyunsaturated fats, a change in body chemistry and its reaction to the sun?

Oils in their natural form (nuts and seeds) appear not to be harmful. It is in their extracted form that trouble arises. This is unsurprising when we examine current methods of commercial extraction. Cold pressed virgin oils are the least damaged products and these are the only ones I use. Extraction involving heating techniques is more likely than not to damage the delicate structures of oils obtained from plants. Heating allows for more oil to be extracted than cold-pressing but chemicals, solvents, bleaching and dyeing are all part of the synthetic process so the food value of the end product has to be questionable.

Oxidation, the bane of the food manufacturer, is a natural progression in the "life span" of a fat: the term we use for a "dead" fat is rancid. Nature, abhorring a vacuum, fills the space along the hydrocarbon chain of an unsaturated fat with oxygen. When the oxidised oil is consumed the oxygen breaks off to form free radicals which prevent the absorption of some minerals such as zinc and can damage cell walls. Manufacturers, in an attempt to prevent spoilage and extend a product's life, introduce anti-oxidising agents into their products, some of which are suspect. Oxidation was not a problem in older traditions where oil was extracted as required; and in some Mediterranean areas the problem of rancidity is overcome by spiking the oil with garlic (a natural anti-oxidising agent).

Oils do not possess the same properties. Using conclusions obtained from Indian studies, Ballantine states that heating corn oil to high temperatures can lead to arteriosclerosis. Safflower oil, touted as the highest in polyunsaturates, is excessively irritating and capable of provoking a wide range of disorders. He also suggests that consumption of large quantities of vegetable oils speeds up the ageing process in the skin, possibly because of the presence of free radicals causing dramatic premature wrinkling.

Fats, most of which should be obtained from seeds and nuts, are a necessary component of a balanced diet. Oils, bought cold-pressed, in small quantities, should be treated with respect and never re-heated. A diet based on whole foods rather than fragmented ones, together with regular exercise, will tolerate some saturated fat (from meat and spreads) and butter is preferable to margarine. I have always included generous amounts of fat in the family diet with no detrimental effects. Used in the same proportion found in human milk, the ratio of fat from all sources is about 25% of the whole diet, which does not accord with current conventional thinking.

[16] Ballantine op.cit. Chapter Five

[17] *"Here's Health"* December 1977

[18] Ballantine op.cit Chapter 5

[19] Ibid Chapter 5

FOOD SUPPLEMENTS
(MINERALS AND VITAMINS)

MINERALS

Confusion about the "safety" of our foods arises because of contradictory advice and from changes of mind by experts. Advocating total bans rather than moderation goes against most people's natural desires and this in itself is dangerous because, when experience does not match the warnings and we do not drop dead after eating a potato crisp or uncooked egg, we become desensitised to all advice on offer. The attitude goes: well if it's going to kill me anyway I may as well enjoy it now. Then, as a precaution, we swallow a handful of vitamin pills to overcome any side-effects and make up any shortfall! And if a particular supplement is endorsed by a celebrity, so much the better. It must be OK. The question is: do we actually need them?

We depend on minerals for proper metabolism and current research insists they cannot be synthesised by the body because much of western science is still based on the Newtonian mechanistic world view and the Cartesian mind-body split. This view holds to the principle of a fixed unit of matter that is neither created nor destroyed and it is a view so ingrained in the very fabric of our society that it is very difficult for material scientists other than the physicists to conceive of anything else.

Despite this belief, the fact is: substances do translate into other substances. During the latter part of the nineteenth century Baron Herzeele of Hanover demonstrated that plants not only transform substances but that the creation of basic elements of matter is commonplace in the organic kingdom. Plants grown in a phosphorus solution lessened the solution's phosphorus content without the seedlings showing any increase in phosphorus. Instead their sulphur content was materially increased. Similarly he showed how plants manufacture phosphorus out of calcium, and magnesium out of carbonic acid.[20]

Rudolph Hauschka proved elements materialise and dematerialise in seedlings according to the phases of the moon. His knowledge underpins the biodynamic system of farming that incorporates a comprehensive knowledge of astronomy into agricultural technique.

According to Ballantine, the French scientist, Louis Kervran, upset the material scientific world when he demonstrated that chickens fed a calcium-free diet created their own calcium so long as the feed contained potassium.[21]

This all goes to prove there is no such thing as a fixed unit of matter and accords wholly with yoga philosophy that has always stated "Matter arises out of Consciousness".

The evidence, a direct contradiction of orthodox scientific dogma, means our innate intelligence will create its own requirements given the means and opportunity: i.e. a balanced environment and a food supply grown in accordance with natural laws.[22]

[20] Hauschka *"The Nature of Substance"* pp 13-14, Ballantine *"Diet and Nutrition"* p 564

[21] Ibid. pp 565-6

[22] Read *"The Healing Power of Illness"* by Thorwald Dethlefsen and Rüdiger Dahlke MD for a comprehensive understanding of the body's innate wisdom.

VITAMINS

Vitamins are organic compounds containing carbon and hydrogen and are found in all foods. Their presence is required for the smooth metabolism of fats, proteins and carbohydrates, the formation of body tissue and cellular energy exchange. At one time it was believed they had to be obtained from the food supply but it is now conceded our bodies have the ability to manufacture some, if not all, of them. It is still widely held that humans, unlike other animals, have lost the ability to synthesise vitamin C yet studies done on human milk in India revealed the vitamin C content to be far in excess of what had been ingested by the mothers in the study.[23]

Anthroposophy teaches us how to look beyond the obviously physical properties of Nature, see what is intended, and thereby unravel the mystery.[24] Rudolph Hauschka explains vitamins [literally vita(life), min(eral)] as currents of energy as opposed to material substance. These currents of energy, neither fixed nor substantial, co-operate in the formation of protein. Anthroposophy describes these etheric formative forces as the lowest level of non-physical reality and they are not to be confused with the hypothetical ether of physicists. There are 4 basic types: A, B, C and D, capable of multiple mutations. E, K, P –as well as all the variations of B –, are simply varieties of their archetype. Synthetic substitutes may be carriers of vitamin action but cannot be relied upon for effectiveness.

If we compare this idea to a CD we would accept that it is not its material but the music imprinted on it that is of value to us. In the same way, the chemical structure of a vitamin is of less account than the energy that forms and uses the substance.

Vitamin	Being	Carrier	Deficiency Symptoms
A	Warmth	Oils (seeds)	Stunted growth
B	Order	Husks	Beriberi
C	Light	Green plants	Scurvy
D	Form	Lipoids	Rickets

VITAMIN A occurs in that part of a plant where warmth is the predominant dynamic – seeds (oils), avocado fruit (fat), and blossoms. Oils burn, revealing the latent fire within. Anthroposophy describes cosmic fire forces at work in the plant and warmth – on the wings of hydrogen – is the expanding, unfolding growth element that allows for seeds to develop into the plant's prototype. In humans stunted growth is the outstanding deficiency disease caused by lack of vitamin A

VITAMIN B is found in the husks, which keep the grains intact. Symptoms of beriberi are loss of support. B gives us shape, form; it orders and regulates the formless; it gives an enclosed boundary. In India when the staple grain food, rice, was husked and the white rice fed to humans, they developed symptoms of beriberi, whereas the chickens fed on the husks, thrived. When the whole-grain was re-introduced the symptoms vanished. The muscles in the ankles of beriberi patients lose the ability to contract; muscle fibres dissolve or separate out, paralysis sets in and nerves degenerate.

VITAMIN C is found in green plants, where photosynthesis takes place. Green leaves are described anthroposophically as being latent LIGHT. Our skin surface is where inner and outer light has to balance for health. Healthy inner light is evidenced in a clear, smooth skin; bright, shiny eyes and rosy cheeks. Lack of vitamin C lends a wilted look, just like a wilted plant. Scurvy patients have a yellowish brown hue, the skin breaks down and bleeds, and other organs involved in the human's light processes such as the kidneys and suprarenal glands also deteriorate.

VITAMIN D is found in lipoids. Cholosterines formed in the liver are in liquid form. These substances are structural materials for the entire organism. Supportive tissue and cell membranes are both composed of it. Our bony structure literally crystallises out of the fluid embryo. Shortage of this vitamin means the basic formative forces lack support and we cannot build up a proper bony structure. D orders or regulates. We require this vitamin for the proper absorption of calcium. Maybe osteoporosis is less to do with lack of calcium than a deficiency in Vitamin D. Our best source of it is fresh air as well as sunlight on our skin – this need not be under a scorching sun. Just plenty of fresh air, even on a cloudy day, on a partially exposed body will do the trick. Synthetic Vitamin D, on the other hand is counterproductive. [25]

Orthomolecular Medicine is the name for the arbitrary supplementary approach to "curing" modern ailments, and is based on the belief that by nourishing the single cell with single nutrients we armour the body against disease. This pre-supposes disease is some external threat always on the alert for an opportunity to invade an unwary body. It is a fear-based concept, rooted in mechanistic principles that hold the parts (i.e. the cell) determine the whole (the body) whereas the holistic view holds the principle in reverse.

We are not designed to ingest and assimilate synthetic Vitamin A as a single nutrient. We are designed to eat carrots which comprise, amongst other organic substances, carotene or vitamin A. If we do substitute the supplement for the whole carrot our bodies become confused and start searching for all the missing "bits" to correct the imbalance. [26] This leads inevitably to cravings, artificial hunger and weight gain, and is the root cause of obesity which is fast reaching the levels of an epidemic in our society.

Since the concept of supplementation was introduced in the USA as an attempt to moderate some of the more drastic effects of junk food, the vitamin industry has burgeoned, in tandem with fast foods, takeaways, and soft drinks. Supplements, alongside branded breakfast cereals and other junk have been artificially synthesised like car fuel. As Colbin succinctly argues, it may be rational to calculate to the nth degree the amount of fuel a car will consume over a given mileage, the car being a machine without an autonomous life force, it is wholly inappropriate to calculate human nutritional needs in the same way because we cannot be standardised. Any synthetic substance can be stripped down to a collection of its basic components and put back together again with no detrimental effects. It will "work" again. This is not true for living substance be it human or a pea.

Strip a pea down to its basic components and stick everything back together again and you will have the illusion of a pea, but the new pea will not feed you as it would have done before it was stripped down because it will be dead. The life force cannot be captured in a laboratory and then re-introduced mechanically into substance to set it going again like a clock. This is precisely what we are trying to do with computers. You may as well try to capture God for analysis, which fundamentally is what all religion is.

As someone I cannot now recall adroitly put it, Religion is not God any more than the plays of Shakespeare or the actors in a play written by Shakespeare are Shakespeare. Yet when actors are speaking words set down in a particular order by Shakespeare, or a collection of his plays are bound together in a book, we recognise Shakespeare in these Works. An aspect of Shakespeare is contained therein, just as God is recognisable in all religions, but that is not to define the man Shakespeare, any more than we can define God absolutely, though we have tried indefatigably from the original moment we separated ourselves mentally from the Whole.

The life force is the organising force that keeps all the individual components of specifics (human beings, peas) interacting or living. You may call this the spirit, or the god aspect of the pea.

This is why homeopathic remedies are valid. What material science will not grasp about the infinitesimal dose of a homeopathic remedy is that succussing raw material loosens the insubstantial from the substantial, (or spirit of that substance,) which is then captivated by, and translated in, solution such as water or alcohol. Why this problem exists within the orthodox medical profession is mystifying when it understands perfectly that if you want to hold nitrogen, a gas, you have to dissolve it in water. Dissolving a gas in water, which unlike a laboratory is also living substance, is only one stage removed from dissolving the spirit or life force of any substance to hold it.

Trials have shown individuals of the same height, colouring, weight, and similar disposition and attitude, fed an identical measured diet will process the food differently. Even twins have demonstrated a 26% differential[27]. Nor are discrepancies confined to individuals: within one person there are variables from day to day or even within the hour depending on his/her emotional and mental state.

Our functioning, our requirements beyond our physiology, depend upon personality and our way of responding to situations. The amount of nutrients each one of us assimilates depends on the functioning of our individual digestive system, and its interacting with our emotional and mental systems.

A healthy body will obtain what it requires from the food supply, provided that food is not inert to begin with, and the richer in nutrients the food, the better the tools the body has to work with.

Advocates of the orthomolecular approach to nutrition often cite the impoverished state of modern foods, grown in nutritionally sub-standard soils, as an argument for supplementation. But the random use of supplements as a precautionary measure indicates mistrust. If we are motivated primarily by a gnawing doubt of insufficiency, we will never experience the satisfaction accruing from "just knowing" the meaning of enough. Not knowing when we have had enough is a curse in western society and a breeding ground for excess. The supplemented diet mirrors this aspect of our nature. The demand for cheap food coupled by the supermarkets' practice of "buy one, get one free" reinforces the habit of sacrificing quality for quantity. If the Law of Karma holds, obesity is the inevitable outcome.

Food values are unstable, we are unstable. Discrepancies in vitamin and mineral content occur not only in foods per se but according to where and how they are grown. Biodynamic and organic produce is of superior quality to that grown in an artificial environment but even this is not the whole picture. Macrobiotic practitioners have demonstrated time and again how human handling, preparation and attitude influence the energetic content of food. This would also accord with the anthroposophical approach to nutrition. I know of no better evidence of the human will's ability to act upon and enhance its monstrously meagre diet than the story of one concentration camp survivor of the last World War. I first heard about this man's experience on the radio sometime during the late 1950s, early '60s, and over the decades the story would re-surface from time to time, a little altered in detail but substantially the same.

Camp liberators at the end of the war were shocked to find such an emaciated scrap of humanity still breathing and, when they learned how long he had endured the camp conditions, his survival seemed to border on the miraculous. He told them that upon arrival at the camp he was struck by the way the inmates, starving and dehumanised, would wolf the one meal of the day. This "meal" was a single potato in a bowl of watery gruel and, realising he would not survive were he reduced to swallowing such rations at a single gulp, he constructed a strategy that would allow him possibility.

From the outset, whilst not condoning their behaviour, he refused to condemn his captors. Each time they doled out the evening ration he would bless them for feeding him. Famished, he would force himself to abstain from immediate gratification and, instead, carried the potato to the perimeter of the camp. Here he sat down and addressed it, mentally going through its entire life cycle by visualising it as a tiny seed emerging from the ground, growing to maturity, being harvested, transported and marketed until it ended up in the camp's pot of gruel. Finally, he gave thanks to the potato for the sacrifice of its life and chewed it slowly, absorbing its very essence into his being. This was his pattern day in, day out over the years he was interred. And this, he claimed, is what sustained him.

The suggestion accords absolutely with the anthroposophical view that holds, contrary to popular misconception, humans are NOT altogether what they eat. Animals are what they eat but we are essentially different from animals insofar as our make-up is determined. In combination with the higher mammals, our physicality contains the 4 basic elemental forms of earth (skeleton), water (body fluids), fire (warm body temperature) and air (breath). In addition we, uniquely, possess a fifth element – ether, which equates with light and translates in us as imagination (we speak of being enlightened). It is this fifth element which is crucial to our self-determination, and Hauschka is particularly illuminating when he describes humans as "their ability to breakdown and overcome their food in order to transubstantiate it into complete human protein."[28] We, in common with the animal kingdom, digest and assimilate our food but we alone possess a will that determines how our organism utilises whatsoever we consume. This is why we express food preferences and why we say: "one man's meat is another's poison". I doubt you would find a lion with a partiality to zebra and not gazelle – it is all meat to lions and, therefore, fair game! It is crucial to grasp this fact if we are ever to understand our relationship with our food supply and the world outside ourselves.

In the final analysis single element substances such as vitamins and minerals, synthetic drugs, cannot truly augment or restore our health, because they themselves are partial, they are not whole. Lacking the life-energy of plants they cannot stimulate the human system to extract what it requires from food to maintain its integrity or to heal.

[23] Rudolph Ballentine op.cit. p 533

[24] Hauschka *"The Nature of Substance"* Chapter 15

[25] Ballantine op.cit. 204-209; also Jacob Lieberman *"Light Medicine of the Future"*

[26] Colbin op.cit.

[27] Ballantine op.cit

[28] Hauschka *"Nutrition"* Chapter on Digestion.

Place the prepared food on the table.

Sit down, ensuring the sitting bones (the bones immediately beneath the buttocks) are connecting with the chair and that this is a comfortable distance away from the table. Ensure the feet are flat on the floor.

Allow the hands to rest comfortably in the lap.

Bring your attention to your solar plexus. Imagine or visualise a light in this area, a candle flame or a pilot light, quietly burning. Feel the warmth spreading throughout this area.

Exhale deeply, allowing the body weight to descend through the pelvis into the chair, down through the legs and feet, into the floor.

Inhaling, allow the spine to release up from the pelvis towards the back of the head. Keep the shoulders relaxed and draw the tips of the shoulder blades down towards the waist.

Keeping the weight of the body grounded on each exhalation will allow the spine to continuously straighten upwards, softly like the stem of a growing plant. Just allow this to occur and de-focus the eyes in order to absorb the table, its contents and surrounds.

See the dishes, plates, implements, food. Become aware of the colours, shapes, and textures, the blends and the contrasts. Become aware of the smells. Allow everything to come towards you. See without looking and permit the senses to sharpen.

Become aware of abundance and sufficiency.

Maintaining your attention at your solar plexus, feel gratitude. Experience the flame of gratitude spreading throughout your body and limbs, to the finger tips and toes. Feel its fulsomeness spreading upwards, through the chest and neck and be absorbed in it and by it.

Experience the saliva gathering in your mouth, close your eyes and exhale deeply. Swallow if necessary.

Open your eyes, be aware of your hands collecting the implements and enjoy your meal.

Chew each mouthful thoroughly and with full awareness until you are finished. If dining alone allow nothing to distract your attention. *[29]

If you are eating in the company of another, conversation is part of the exchange and interchange of the whole meal. Silence is not a prerequisite when dining with others.

Time 2 minutes.

[29] Soft music in the background can be an aid to digestion but it should never be intrusive.

A COMMON SENSE APPROACH TO EATING

Select your foods intuitively rather than intellectually

Pay attention to how you feel before, during and after you eat. Taste and smell are natural guides. Eating what is "good for you" when you don't like it is unwise, eating what someone else tells you is good for you is sheer lunacy.

Eat slowly and with full attention

Chew each mouthful thoroughly. Thorough ensalivation of your food is a form of pre-digestion and also helps you not to over-eat. Taking time over your food will develop your appreciation for your food and yourself.

The digestive system mirrors the mind. Never eat when upset, in a bad mood, watching TV or reading. How our body handles any food will be more important than the food itself.

Eat a balanced diet comprising of a variety of foods

This will ensure you obtain all the nutrients you need and will lessen an inclination to snack. More importantly, you will be less likely to resort to supplements!

Eat fresh seasonal locally produced foods

Try to obtain organic food wherever possible; it is better for you and the environment.

Dried, canned, frozen and prepared foods contain more fat, salt and sugar than we need. They contain additives that we definitely do not need. And they impair our sensitivity to taste. Avoid irradiated, GM, and synthetic foods.

Eat less rather than to satiation point

Eating is a process not an intellectual exercise like cramming the brain with facts in order to get somewhere on the career ladder. Cramming the body with nutrients is counter-productive and over-eating is guaranteed to stress the entire system. In yoga there is a saying: eat to two thirds capacity and leave one third empty for the space in between to digest and assimilate into fullness (wholesomeness).

If we leave the table feeling we could eat a little bit more we avoid obesity. The human has evolved over aeons of time; for most of this food was scarce rather than plentiful and the organism is simply not designed to be fattened up like a turkey for Christmas.

Value simple foods

Eat mostly whole, un-fragmented, foods. Your sense of taste will sharpen and will develop a sense of satisfaction for natural foods. It will also lessen a craving for novelty.

Novelty foods and intellectual recipes are for occasional treats rather than daily use lest we lose our sense of balance and start seeking sensation instead of nutrition. It is the mind that incessantly searches for novelty, not the body, which is always satisfied provided it obtains all the nutrients it is designed to absorb for its functions. If we allow our bodies to lead in matters nutritional we will avoid those twin plagues: craving and addiction.

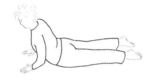

INTERACTING WITH FOOD
(for good or ill)

INTRODUCTION

According to Dr. Ballantine, "It will require a revolution in philosophical thinking for Western science to apprehend that…..living matter is the product of intelligence rather than the origin of intelligence" [1] Yet on a very superficial level it is a given that human mental capacity (Thought) influences and manipulates Matter. Every single human creation started with a thought in someone's head. Conversely Matter (in this instance Foods) will affect us mentally as well as physically to one degree or another.

Selecting foods consciously to support our *consuming* interests, our passion, is more likely to develop mental clarity, emotional contentment and a sense of real fulfilment, whereas mindless consumption, comprising mostly manufactured junk, will increase a capacity for mental confusion, emotional turmoil and can actively impede us from fulfilling our potential. It has been suggested that, to date, the human being manifests a mere 10% of his/her potential and that even Einstein demonstrated only 25% of his. Furthermore a connection has been established between the consumption of junk food and obesity and hyperactivity.

There is a difference between junk as opposed to "right" foods. Junk food is junk food; whereas "right" foods are not right in themselves, they are natural foods that may be "right" for some people and "wrong" for others. Foods are essentially neutral: how an individual personality *interacts* with a particular food and at a particular time will determine whether it has a benign or adverse effect.

I suggest that if you enjoy heavy manual work such as building roads, digging ditches or gardening, a wholly fruitarian diet may be too insubstantial to support you, leaving you feeling physically exhausted; and likewise, if you are engaged in metaphysics, a heavy meat-based diet may "weigh you down".

And it is as well to remember that how much and what we consume are of equal importance. Buddhist philosophy emphasises "the middle way": too much or too little of anything in our lives produces a detrimental effect. Too much food/drink will induce vomiting or obesity, too little and we starve. Too many eggs will constipate mentally (as well as physically); eating nuts daily can have the opposite effect. Consider what these two foods are designed by Nature to become: the one will develop into a fully fledged chicken that scratches the ground, the other into an enormous expansive tree that branches out into space.

Language so often encapsulates the deeper truths of the human drama: someone who does not appear rational is often referred to as "nutty".

In the same way as all people are endowed with personalities, all foods are endowed with particular properties. Coffee, for instance, is a natural product. Food fascism is currently condemning coffee consumption even though it may be perfectly feasible for some people to include some coffee in their diet. If you are engaged vocationally in an occupation demanding you think logically and linearly, coffee will support this type of mental activity.[2] Coffee is the student beverage of choice. People working in marketing, planning, journalism and investigation would possibly benefit from drinking coffee. A career change in an opposite direction could equally lead to a decrease or even abstention from coffee. Nature requires we consume what allows us to feel well: I have known highly motivated career-women consume copious quantities of coffee and then, almost as a matter of course, eschew it upon becoming pregnant. So forget ideas about "right diet" for all people for all times.

Good health is our natural state of being and is continuously adjusting, so it is likely our dietary preferences will alter as we alter direction during the course of our life. When I became interested in the more esoteric aspects of yoga I inclined towards a strict vegetarian diet. Some years into the practice I developed a more practical approach that required me to become more grounded *mentally* as much as physically. Unaware that I needed to adapt my diet, I started to develop physical symptoms of anaemia. This was a strong signal from my body that the foods I was consuming were too insubstantial to support me on all levels.

I addressed this, eventually, by including some fish in my diet and I came to realise that flexibility applies to more than physical yoga practice. Had I not adjusted my diet I suspect I would now be "floating somewhere out there in the ether", mentally spaced out and supplementing with bottles of iron pills! It isn't just the banned substances that send us into altered states of consciousness!!

Life, in all its dimensions, changes. Before the Second World War the majority of people living in Britain were born, lived and died within the same community; sons followed fathers down mines, daughters, mothers into factories etc. In other words, where you were born and the social status into which you were born determined your life experience to a large extent. This is no longer the case. Today individuals migrate, we cross social boundaries and we no longer expect to pursue a single job or career during the course of our working lives. There is a much greater degree of diversity everywhere. And this is reflected in eating patterns.

However, where a particular food may enhance wellbeing and support us towards fulfilment of our myriad goals, no food can transform us into something we are not. There is no "magic pill" effect that will spin gold out of straw.

No more than a rose can become a lily, if we are designed by Nature to dance no diet is of itself going to enable us to express ourselves as statisticians or brain surgeons. The most food can do is provide a framework of support that allows for a smooth transition between caterpillar and butterfly.

Nor can any food make us happy: A favourite food may delight and entrance us, causing an emotional uplift; but this lift is transitory and cannot be sustained indefinitely, or habitually. Taste ice cream and experience heaven; eat enough and we soon sicken of it when it fails to deliver its initial buzz. Happiness is a state of being – not an event.

[1] Ballantine op.cit. p573

[2] Anne-Marie Colbin op.cit

ATTENTION TO FOOD

Animals are endowed by Nature with skills that allow them to obtain foods suited to their needs. They have to survive on what they can get with no opportunity for embellishment. Humans, on the other hand, have the capacity to improve and enhance their diet through selection, culinary artifice, flavouring and presentation. In addition, humans can affect the quality of a food's energy with their mental capacities provided that food is not inert (junk) to begin with. This begins with selection and ends with consumption, and the degree to which the food's quality is enhanced depends on the individual's power of attention.

We cannot measure this enhancement; we can only experience it. Go to any market where fresh foods are displayed unwrapped. Appearance is paramount. We are drawn initially as much by eye as by foot towards making a purchase. At a glance eyes imbibe colour, shape, texture and size, discarding the pallid in favour of the bright, differentiating between the limp and robust, the regular from the irregular, the wholesome from the unwholesome.

Observe outstretched hands hovering over the produce, like dragonflies sensing substance. Bird-like they dart and dive, picking over what they want, turning it to ascertain texture. Heads incline sharply to ingest the aroma, to distinguish the fresh from the stale. Only then is decision reached, and on a satisfied exhalation, the produce is handed across for pricing and wrapping, and an exchange is completed through the medium of money. All this, and scarcely an intellectual thought rippling the brain cells.

This is only the beginning of the relationship. We choose the food. That makes the relationship personal. Maintaining the relationship continues with appropriate storage until the food is required for preparation and processing. It concludes with consumption, digestion and assimilation. All these stages require attention.

Attention is not concentration. Concentration is narrow, singular, and active. It requires effort to sustain it; and we need to develop its capacity when we want to pass exams or engage in methodology. Attention is broad, open, passive and absorbing. It allows information in. Like God, it is a centre without a circumference, and is the capacity to see without looking. Concentration looks at what has been created, attention is creative. Concentration requires an object and a subject, attention is both subject and object together.

Attention is pure energy and, as modern physicists would allow, is both the particle and the wave. Whenever we place our attention in anything the thing becomes energised and relatively "us". Full attention occupies one wholly without the intervention of distraction. To quote Krishnamurti "attention is meditation".

We have a choice. We can select and eat our foods with indifference, or with half a mind on what we are doing (inattention) and the food will nourish us according to the energy levels present in the food. Or, with full awareness we can place our attention in the food, and augment the energies present in that food with our own. On the physical plane it equates with boosting mobile phone batteries with an electrical charger. To paraphrase the late Timothy Leary, we turn on, tune in, and merge.

It is not a concept that can be scientifically demonstrated or "proven", it has to be experienced to be valid. Any "evidence" I can offer is anecdotal which in itself will be insufficient for materialists or sceptics, but it might serve as a launching pad for the curious or open-minded. The story of the prisoner-of-war, related in the previous section will serve as one example. When I taught wholefood cookery, students would sometimes comment that a recipe we had devised did not taste quite the same as when I made it. We all used the same measured ingredients, and cooked the food at the same temperature, and with the same care. In the end we concluded that the intrinsic factor absent was possibly the application of full attention, a practice in which I was fluent where they were not.

Physicists accept that thoughts are waves of energy. Modern medicine allows that positive thoughts and visualisations affect the healing process. Thoughts either influence matter or they do not. Consensus of opinion has it that they do. Mystics have always advanced this concept and a verse from the Buddhist tradition aptly illustrates it:

Sow a thought and reap an idea
Sow an idea and reap a belief
Sow a belief and reap a habit
Sow a habit and reap a character
Sow a character and reap a personality
Sow a personality and reap an individual.

Thoughts are energy waves operating at a higher frequency than matter. The power is demonstrable inasmuch as every **thing** in existence on this planet from the pyramids to a pair of Levis originated as a thought in someone's head. If human **beings** can create machines of sufficient sophistication to measure and explore our Universe, it is no big deal for them to turn this power towards the very substance that nurtures their continuance.

The idea that talking to plants assists their growth ceased to be risible as more and more people engaged in the practice, and verified it. Sensitives like the late Dr. Bach held the principle in reverse. In his case plants communed with him. Flower Remedies have subsequently become part of the human pharmacology, used in the restoration of emotional health. Bringing flowers to the sick is traditional. Some innate wisdom comprehends that the flowers' energy interacts with our own to help bring us up to strength.

This may be a step too far for some but the most sceptical amongst us will allow that flowers invariably bring a smile to the face of the recipient and we sense an immediate lift in the spirits of the downhearted. Children instinctively bring flowers to their mothers. Remember the cherished dandelion your child believed a rose? The exchange of smiles between a child and a world-weary adult is heart melting. I love the saying "If you see someone without a smile, give them yours". It is truly a habit worth cultivating. Communing without words is powerful: it is an exchange of energy from heart to heart.

It is immensely absorbing, and satisfying, being able to interact with one's food, particularly where that food has not been obtained from the best sources or produced under optimum conditions. For preference I choose fresh organic produce wherever possible but if I can only get commercially produced cabbage I will use that, and will be grateful for it. I would rather have raw milk than pasteurised but since that is denied me I'll take what is available and adapt where necessary. But I will not use synthetic "foods" or food past its sell-by date, by which I mean food that is dead or rotten. Wilted vegetables are as much beyond redemption as a rigid fish, rancid butter or a smelly chicken.

When I stopped eating meat I expected to continue cooking it for those members of the family who liked it. Years later I was still inventing fresh ways of serving up meat dishes and friends puzzled over how it was possible to invent meat sauces and gravies without tasting. I have no rational explanation and can only explain that somehow I "taste" them in my head whilst I'm making them. I suppose this practice belongs in the realms of being able to communicate with plants!

Not so long ago intelligence was equated with intellectual capacity. In this country the 11 plus exam was the accepted means of determining the sheep from the goats or, to put it more bluntly, the bright from the "thick". It proved wholly inappropriate and we now know that intelligence manifests itself in a multitude of capacities. At the last count I heard there are at least nine ways of measuring it and in due course we will discover many more, like planets. Recently we discovered the tenth planet of our solar system! Was not Sedna, like Chiron before it, always there just waiting to reflect in human consciousness?

I suspect that one reason we are reluctant to admit to the power of subtle energies is that they are invisible. Westerners like to be able to handle proof so we can measure it. We cannot handle electricity but the fact that we can experience its effects allows for common acceptance of electricity's existence. We need to be certain because, understandably, we do not want to delude ourselves, which is why, at the beginning of my yoga classes I always say, "Do not *believe* anything I say. Listen to my suggestion and then try it out for yourself." Indirect experience (someone else's truth) is no substitute for direct experience (my truth). This book is based on my own experience, and what I have verified for myself from other people's, and is offered only as an opportunity to explore and find out if any of my truths ring true for you too. Wanting to share, be it food, thoughts or feelings, is part of the human make-up.

For those unconvinced of the possibility of the intrinsic power of attention, I needs must again fall back on Shakespeare, and suggest "There are more things in heaven and earth, Horatio, than are dreamed of in your philosophy." (Hamlet. Act 1 Scene 4)

THE WORLD AS DUALITY

The world, as perceived by our present consciousness, presents itself as a duality, a combination of apparent opposites. For every back there is a front, an up and a down, an inhalation and exhalation. We experience our world both spiritually and materially: on the one hand the Mind allows us to form concepts out of anything that is "not us", which equates with spiritual digestion; on the other we digest the substantial world as food. This is material digestion. Material and spiritual digestion are interdependent, and are potentially sublimated into the state of Oneness / Wholeness through the individual.

In yoga terminology this duality would be understood as the Universal Principle (which in itself is indivisible and beyond the grasp of the human's five senses) differentiating into two antagonistic and complementary tendencies of expansion and contraction, time and space, beginning and end or yin and yang. These 2 primary forces can be called movement and rest. Physics refers to the particle and the wave.

If we pay attention to our body's responses to what we are eating, and to our mental attitudes, we will learn to choose balanced foods or foods which combine to balance naturally, and our eating patterns will balance.

We will select warm and cool, hot and cold, fresh and dried, cooked and raw, according to our needs, and these will vary according to season, habitat, and *how we are* at any particular time. Staying alert to our own and other people's needs on all levels makes for a life of adventure and constant change rather than one of boredom, habit, and a sense of alienation.

Harmony is one of the principle laws whereby yin and yang are always balancing in different dimensions at all stages of the changing process. Each being is constantly realising a harmony within itself as well as a harmony with external conditions. Where this law does not apply, dis-harmony leads to dis-ease. If we introduce harmony into our diet, our lives can harmonise on other levels as well; we will work and rest, socialise and allow time for personal reflection.

The two forces, yin and yang, do not act destructively against each other but serially, as opposite factors, to maintain balance: upward motion causes downward motion as the next step; faster becomes slower and slower faster. The exhalation leads into an inhalation which moves into another exhalation. Hunger leads to satisfaction and assimilation which leads once more to hunger.

There are no independent manifestations arising separately out of time, everything is connected with the past. There are no mutations and accidents in the modern sense occurring in the universe – EVERYTHING has its cause and everything becomes the next process in its change. Babies born defective, hyperactivity, stress, heart disease are not simply questions of ill luck. In each case the cause is due to some past action which can either be perceived or not. The Law of Karma is the Law of Cause and Effect.

In some cases we may have to comb through generations to find the contributing factor to a given condition. Many latter-day health problems are currently being attributed to our genes, our historical biological map. This is not to attribute blame. Blame suggests guilt and if we have guilt it follows we have to have innocence. From a universal perspective neither guilt nor innocence is more worthy than the other. The idea of the sins of the father being visited on the son is valid only if you take the word sin in its original context, which means being "off the mark", off course rather than bad or wicked as it has come to mean today.

In other cases it is easier to locate the cause: if I consume a bottle of whisky it is likely that I will behave in a drunken manner. And if I then drive a car and have "an accident" in which I kill someone, that person dies as a result of what I did not because some malign deity decided to put the victim in my way and at the same time impaired my vision and motor functions.

Everything is connected in the process of time and space.

**YIN AND YANG
APPLIED TO FOOD**

Food is the mode of evolution whereby one species transforms into another.

Yin energy creates growth and more rapid growth in a hot climate. Yin foods comprise more water than yang foods and have the tendency for upward growth above the ground.

Yang energy creates growth in a cold climate, and slower growth. Drier foods, stems, roots and seeds are expressions of yang forces. They are nurtured by contracting energies: downward growth below ground (root vegetables).

Since we are involved in constant change nothing can be said to be wholly yin or wholly yang, only more yin or more yang.

In the meat category red meat is more yang than white meat. Beef, mutton and pork would be considered more yang than poultry and in the poultry category turkey and duck (darker coloured meat) would be considered more yang than chicken (lighter coloured meat). Poultry is more yang than fish.

With some minor exceptions most plant food is more yin than yang because of some of the following attributes:

• Plants materialise in a more expansive form – branches, leaves, growing outward and upward from, or laterally along, the ground. Animal bodies are formed in an inward direction with compact organs and cells.

• Body temperatures of plants are cooler than some species of animal; they inhale carbon dioxide and exhale oxygen whereas animals do the reverse.

• Plants are represented by the "cool" colour green (chlorophyll) while animals are represented by the "hot" colour red (haemoglobin).

However, within each species yin and yang continues to manifest:

• Fruits are said to be more yin than vegetables because they are generally more expanded in shape, sweeter and more watery.

• Among fruits the smaller, harder ones such as apples are more yang than oranges which are larger and softer.

• Among apples from the same tree, nutrients and energy can differ depending on which side of the tree they grow, the height at which they grow on the tree, and the season – even the time of day at which they are picked. A sweet red eating apple (Gala) is more yang than a similar sized green, cooking apple (Bramley).

Examples of Yin and Yang represented by foods

Strong Yang	More Balanced	Strong Yin
Refined salt	Unrefined sea salt	
Canned foods	Beans, bean products	Frozen foods
Eggs	Soya curd (tofu)	
	Roots, leafy greens	Tropical fruit & veg.
Cheese	Sea vegetables	Milk, cream, yoghurt
	Local fruit	Ice cream
Poultry	Whole cereal grains	White flours, white rice
Meat	Unrefined vegetable oils	Refined oils
	Spring water	Spices
Fish	Non-aromatic, non-stimulant teas and beverages	Aromatic, stimulant teas and coffee
	Seeds, nuts	Honey, sugar
		Alcohol, drugs,
		Chemicals

THE POWER OF COLOUR

"Light, being one of our major forms of nutrition, not only affects our bodies directly but also affects us indirectly through the foods we eat. Most foods are actually light in solid form"[3]

The world outside our self is colour. We literally live in light and experience this light separated out into individual colours. A mystic friend informs me that humans have not always seen the spectrum visible to us today, that earlier human consciousness permitted a much duller perception, a world greyer than our own. I have no means of proving this. What I do know is that when my energy levels are low the world seems to be less vividly coloured than when they are high. Animals, I am told, experience the world as black and white. I have no means of verifying this either. And what do blind people experience? Probably as many variations as anyone else. Jacques Lusseyerans, the late French philosopher and resistance fighter of the last World War, was blinded in an accident, yet he "saw" as clearly as when he was sighted. He continued to experience the world in vivid colour. The most likely explanation for this is that the accident affected his pineal gland in that it opened up his "third eye". In yoga terms this is the sixth chakra or energy centre, located just above the centre of the forehead. Many people experience this chakra operating during meditation, and it is a transitory experience. In Lusseyerans' experience his third eye stayed open. In his own words he felt more sighted after his accident than before it and experienced no more difficulty in moving around than a sighted person. Yet officially he was designated blind.

Knowingly or unknowingly we are all affected by colours which differentiate according to the frequency at which they are vibrating, red being the longest and strongest wavelength available to our power of perception, and violet the shortest and most ephemeral to our senses.

We recognise colours by a given name. For example a parent teaching a child its colours will point to the bus and say RED, then to a tomato and repeat RED and so on until the child picks up on the concept and points to a red object and says RED. So far so good, but how do we know the child is seeing the exact shading of red that the parent is seeing? The short answer is we don't. We have no idea whether anyone of us is seeing the exact same shade of a particular colour as anyone else, and the reason is that the sharpness of colours is elusive and how *we are* at any one moment will determine what we are actually seeing.

Nevertheless we expect to experience colour in common. My husband is red-green blind and I was confused when I realised the red coat I was wearing looked green to him and my green eye shadow was red. I think what disturbed me most was that he wasn't seeing what I thought I was projecting (we were both single at the time and I was still trying to impress him!) He was not in the least perturbed: he "saw" a red coat because he had been taught RED for the colour he was experiencing. This is fortunate for the population as a whole because there are many red-green blind men and I hate to think what would happen at traffic lights if they begged to differ over what is GREEN and RED.

Colours affect us differently and this includes coloured foods that may be expressed as light in solid form. Before any food reaches our mouth, we ingest it visually. Appetite can be heightened or lowered according to how food is presented, and most of all by its colour-full-ness. When I serve lunch for my yoga students on our monthly workshops their first response is always to the food's colours.

When planning a menu I decide upon the main feature and then incorporate the rest according to seasonal availability, texture, shape and, most of all colour. This does not end with the food. The serving dishes, cloth, crockery and surrounds have to harmonise. In winter I use a lot of red, orange colours because these are instinctively warming and balance the season's opposing polarity which is cold. In summer foods come to the table in full spectrum with the emphasis on greens blending to white in one direction (salads, peppers, celery, white rice) and red in the other – fruits include oranges, mango, peaches, blueberries, raspberries and strawberries. Spring likes lots of yellow.

How foods are organised makes a difference too. My chickpea casserole, which is bright yellow, requires separating from the bowl of white potato with a dish of orange-red roasted vegetables whilst on its other side it likes a tureen of dark green cabbage, purple sprouting broccoli or creamed spinach. If the main dish is placed in the centre of the table, ensure the side dishes blend rather than argue. Red is dramatic and can be bossy, so tone it down with olives, broccoli, onion, cauliflower or turnip. Green dances, it needs substance to bring it to heel, so bring on the puréed swede and butternut. Salmon's delicate pink appreciates tenderness, so look for peas, mangetouts or baby broad beans, sweet corn and new potatoes. Aubergine equates with Spanish flamenco; its dark glossy cloak can be partnered with skirts of red peppers, red onions and beefsteak tomato. Strips of carrot, parsnip and celery, tied with a silk ribbon of leeks, make an attractive nosegay and marry well with spears of asparagus in a hollandaise sauce. Any simple meal such as sliced meat in gravy or plain steamed fish, accompanied by potato, and one other vegetable can be enhanced by a vase of fresh flowers in the centre of the table.

Lieberman goes on to say," The potency or nutritional value of light in food is directly related to the quality of the food carrying its force." He suggests that foods low down the food chain (nuts, fruits, whole grains, and vegetables) nourish us better than those higher up the food chain (animal products) because the former are closest to receiving the light's full force. Junk (synthetic), irradiated, heavily processed, frozen, or fast foods, are deficient or devoid of light's nutritional value. This is just another way of saying fresh food is superior to manufactured food or that processed foods are vitamin deficient and not improved by the addition of artificial supplements because a dead food, like John Cleese's infamous parrot, is always dead.

And he concludes "Eating nutritionally dead food eventually starves our bodies, minds and spirits, creating diminished function, frequent illness, chronic illness, and finally death itself."[4]

[3] Jacob Lieberman *"Light: Medicine of the Future"* p 159.

[4] Lieberman op.cit. p 159

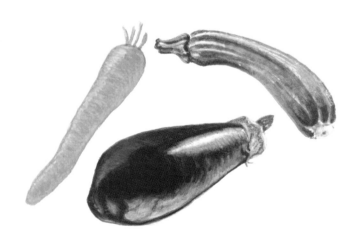

COOKING WITH ATTENTION

Factory produced foods do not require attention beyond measurement and prevention. This is really not attention at all, but concentration and is why, in the interests of efficiency, machinery has been developed to "sense" any inadvertent contamination. Machinery cannot be made attentive, because attention is variable and a uniquely human quality, not a property or a constant.

A complaint I hear frequently about ready-made meals is "they all taste the same." Obviously a curry, chop suey, risotto or packet of vegetarian bangers and mash, will taste recognisably different from each other. What is implied is that pre-packaged meals have a recognisable "sameness" quality to them, like a signature or thread running through the food. Buying different brands makes no appreciable difference. Possibly some contain ingredients in common but, more importantly, they have all been mass-produced which means they are made to a standard. The whole point of such food is the standardisation, so that quality can be measured. A brand of baked beans will taste the same the world over year in, year out.

Any predictable taste, whether factory or home made, dulls the appetite over time and staying attentive to it is difficult. In some instances repetition not only renders foods bland, they cease to be tasted at all! As a child my husband came to know what day of the week it was by what he was given for dinner: roast on Sunday, cold on Monday, stew on Tuesday, mince on Wednesday and so on. This is not to malign his mother, who is an excellent cook, but the package holiday abroad and mass-introduction to international cuisine had not yet materialised. Coupled with food rationing, we can be certain choice then would not equate with what we have now. Mince 50 years ago would be plain mince or rissoles, not bolognaise, kebab or curry.

Cookery programmes have become favourite viewing over recent years. What is striking about TV chefs is less their individual style and artifice than the enthusiasm they have in common, the total involvement in what they are presenting. Anyone can follow a recipe; no one can imitate flair or passion, which has to be felt to be expressed; and this, I suggest, is what differentiates an efficient cook from a successful chef.

No matter what I am making, be it a sandwich or a five-course meal I feel it is important to give the foods involved my full attention.

IN CONCLUSION: "FOOD FOR THOUGHT"

KEEPING AN OPEN MIND

What I am about to relate is a true tale which speaks volumes about our tendency for pre-judgment and expectation.

Between 1991 and 2003 I spent most of my time in a variety of northern penal institutions, teaching yoga and, occasionally, cookery. In one of these prisons, having established a sound relationship with one particular class, I felt confident enough to experiment with novelty, which entailed bringing food into the classroom setting.

The idea was that in place of the normal yoga session, I would cook for the students and introduce them to a lunch based on a Buddhist ritual. This meant lunch would be a longer than normal, somewhat drawn out affair, and entailed the students remaining behind after class instead of returning to their cells at the end of the morning.

Anyone who has ever worked in a prison will understand the difficulties this would present owing to procedures, timetables and logistics necessary for the smooth operation of any regime, not to mention regulations. However, my request was granted, I enjoyed the full co-operation of my line manager and prison officers, and I remain grateful to them all.

Obviously I needed to ascertain the men's co-operation so, *the proposed menu excepted,* the students were fully briefed the week beforehand. This also allowed for questions so that they understood exactly what was required of them. They were "up for it" so I was sanguine about the outcome.

The menu had to incorporate all five tastes as well as a variety of shapes, textures, and colours so I spent the entire morning before the yoga session occupied in the cookery room, where I cooked from scratch a variety of seasonal organic vegetarian dishes. The men were all meat eaters. How they would handle the "foreign" food was part of the experiment.

The cookery room had a carpeted area with desks and chairs for theory: this was cleared. I spread a large, white cloth over it and arranged yoga blocks in a semicircle around the perimeter. The men entered the room in silence, sat down and assumed a cross-legged posture, hands folded in laps, while I set the food before them. I handed round plates, cutlery, napkins and glasses of water and joined them in the one remaining space.

For some moments we simply sat, softly focusing on the food. After a few minutes a group breathing rhythm established itself. At some point one of the group members broke rank, picked up the dish nearest him and offered it to his neighbour on his left who indicated acceptance with an upturned palm and, when he had sufficient, turned his palm down. The dish was then offered to the person on his right and, when this man had sufficient, the dish was replaced on the floor to be picked up by someone else and passed round. In the meantime, the other students had followed suit, supplying their neighbours with the dishes nearest to hand and at no time helping themselves to food. Eventually all the dishes were passed around and eating commenced, in total silence.

When a student had finished, he set down his plate and re-folded his hands in his lap. If he wanted more, he had to wait for someone to notice his situation and then proffer a dish to which he would indicate yes or no with the same turn of palm.

No-one was allowed to ask for food at anytime and if he felt himself ignored or overlooked he had to accept the situation whilst monitoring his emotions. Bear in mind some of these men were serving sentences for violent behaviour: patience and forbearance were not necessarily part of any individual's social patterning.

When the meal was completed, I cleared away the dishes, glasses, cutlery and crockery and resumed my place. Then, placing my hands together in namaste (prayer position at the centre of the chest), I bowed towards each student in turn, and he responded in the same manner to me, and I then bowed to the floor and placed my forehead on the ground. Each student then bowed to his neighbour to left and to right.

Only then was silence broken and a veritable dawn chorus was let loose. When the clamour died down it allowed for individual feedback. To my delight every man waxed lyrical about the vegetarian food and I am not sure who was the more surprised, the carnivores or me! Everyone had found the experience uplifting, they had enjoyed the slowness of the meal, they had enjoyed thoroughly chewing the food, they had enjoyed being responsible for their fellows and they spoke about the sense of peace that was exuded. Most of all they spoke gratitude, and one man ventured he would never look upon food in the same way again. I was choked to silence.

When it was time to leave, an officer collected them and told me afterwards he had never seen prisoners so content. Apparently they were "buzzing" all the way back to the wings.

The food I had cooked was "foreign" to these men's palettes, yet it was accepted in the spirit in which it had been offered, and demonstrated a generosity on their part beyond anything I could have anticipated. For my part their acceptance and participation in the ritual fulfilled the adage that: if we can meet Life with no expectation we can never be disappointed.

There are many reasons why people come to yoga: some regard it as a form of exercise whereby they can become more flexible, others are attracted intellectually by the philosophy, some find the practice relaxing, and there are those who are drawn to it as a means of developing their spiritual practice. Yoga will satisfy all these needs, according to what the individual is seeking, which is why there are so many different approaches and emphases. No matter what route or path is taken benefits accrue through the practice. However, when yoga becomes a way of life it becomes you.

If Life can be described essentially as movement between two points, then posture is shaped movement. Like the pause between the inhalation and exhalation, any posture is simply movement at rest. All posture whether classical yoga or natural body positioning needs to be comfortable with smooth transitions in between. For ease of external movement, the energy needs to continue flowing internally. We can sit motionless but, inside, life continues to flow as involuntary movement (the heartbeat, the breathing, the brain's electrical activity, expansion-contraction at cellular level). And for the body to be supple the spine has to be able to release – continuously.

When the human body is aligned correctly, external forces or energies such as gravity, can act upon it efficiently and the entire organism is wholly at ease. When it is mis-aligned we suffer from discomfort and the organism is occupied in endeavour to rebalance. Yoga teaches awareness of body and mind so that natural adjustments can take place to restore harmony. Without the awareness, the body's capacity for free movement is either limited or only ever a potential. On the one hand the body fidgets and struggles to find a comfortable position, which dissipates energy and leads to premature ageing and chronic dis-ease. On the other hand, never discovering the body's natural capacity is like trying to drive a car in neutral; the journey is unfulfilled. We will never know of what we are capable unless we allow ourselves the magic of self-discovery.

Yoga is for everyone: all that is required is a body, the ground, the gravitational pull, the breath and the attention. The attention is the key without which everything remains potential instead of actual experience.

Attention is unforced, it observes rather than censors, and it never interferes. The most difficult part of yoga practice is to resist doing anything to alter what is present . If our powers of observation show us one shoulder lifted higher than the other it is very difficult not to make an adjustment.

Of course we can impose our will and force the body to conform to a predetermined pattern; try anything hard enough and there is often the power to succeed, but the price is high. We end up adding more stress to an already stressed organism or situation until we reach breaking point. This is not yoga, it is ambition, and its power derives from concentration not attention.

Doing nothing when we have been raised from infancy to do something is almost impossible at first, but with patience, we learn the wisdom of just watching and waiting. The body, in its own time, at its own pace, given the opportunity and means will right itself. The wisdom is already there in the cells and it unfolds from within, out.

The joy of witnessing this happening is indescribable, and incredibly powerful. Which is why the ego, at first, feels slighted: it has had to relinquish its control. This is what the mystics from the Buddha, to Jesus and Mohammed, and many before them and still more to come after them, mean when they speak of "letting go". Trust, yielding to some other power, does not sit well with our ego. Its nature is designed to organise and alter whatever does not suit it. This is the illusion, the maya so frequently referred to by the texts, prophets and gurus. This power higher than the ego does not have to be sought for

the simple reason it is already there, within us, waiting to be accessed. There is nothing to prove just everything to see.

Naturally, if a body is missing a limb or has had corrective surgery, no amount of attention will alter that, which is not to say that this body cannot reorganise itself and rebalance to whatever capacity it can attain *now*.

At first it is difficult to maintain the attention. Our mind wanders and we appear to lose it but with patience paying attention becomes easier, as the ego grudgingly accepts it and eventually befriends it. If we practise paying attention in all the little everyday activities, it strengthens until we find we are attentive as a matter of course.

The kitchen is an ideal place for practice simply because meal preparation involves us so intimately in the world outside our self: it is a hands-on experience of colour, texture, shape, tastes, sounds and smells. All the senses are heightened to a degree I have not discovered elsewhere. Whether I am cooking or on my mat I am practising yoga, so long as I am paying full attention. Without the attention it is just routine, and relatively lifeless.

One of the most frequent comments I hear as a yoga teacher is "I'd love to take up yoga, if only I had the time." Time or lack of it seems to be one of the main reasons given for not practising; this includes myself and, possibly, other teachers. So I have devised a system for when circumstance does not permit the luxury of a two hour practice, and it can be used by anyone in reasonable health*, even those who would never consider attending a yoga class but who would appreciate a little more ease in their lives.

Note: **SAFEGUARDS**

If you have a health problem, have recently undergone surgery, are in the early or latter stages of pregnancy or have any doubts about whether you should embark on an exercise regime, please consult your health practitioner before embarking on any of the outlined programmes.

As a general rule:

People with high blood pressure or heart problems are advised not to take their arms above shoulder level, and should refrain from taking the head below the heart when forward bending.

Diabetics should refrain from strong spinal rotations.

Pregnancy – wait until the beginning of the second trimester before starting the practice, and avoid lying on your back during the third trimester. At ALL stages be guided by your midwife or doctor.

A BASIC PRACTICE FOR NOVICES IN 4 STAGES

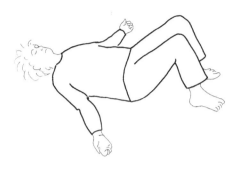

Repeat each stage of the practice at regular intervals until you are familiar with it before moving onto the next stage. It is helpful to practise at the same time each day / week because this establishes a routine like cleaning your teeth. **This practice is not advocated for pregnancy.**

STAGE 1   Time: 20 minutes

- If someone can read these instructions to you as you practise so much the better. If not read them through to yourself a few times until you familiarise them to yourself mentally.

- Wear loose comfortable clothing, have the feet bare and ensure you will not be disturbed. Be prepared to move if at any time you become uncomfortable, you can always revert back to the base position.

- Lie on your back and check that your chin can roll down towards your throat without constricting it; if this is impossible or difficult, place a book about 3 cm in depth under the back of your head.

- Rest the centre of the back of your head (the area between your ears) on the floor or the book. Close your eyes and relax your jaw by separating your back teeth slightly. As the chin releases to some extent in the direction of your throat, notice how the upper part of the back of your neck responds. Is it stiff or easy?

- Bend your knees, allowing the heels to come as close to your seat as is comfortable.

- Position the feet so that they face forwards, about hip width apart. Allow them to "find" the floor, their natural home. Check that the pelvis is comfortable. Experiment by slightly turning the fronts of the feet in towards each other; if this feels better leave them there; if it makes no significant difference, turn them forwards again.

- Lift the toes and let them go; allow them to lengthen forwards and feel the pads of the toes softly connect with the floor. Develop a sense of space between and through each toe. Observe where the weight is falling through the foot. Imagine a triangle across the ball of the foot from the base of the big toe to the root of the little toe, and the centre of the base of the heel. Sense the foot being gently pulled from below through the points of this triangle and allow the foot to balance naturally. Remember this may not happen the first time you practise, just observe any resistance to the suggestion.

- When the foot is balanced the ankles will align; you may feel a space or an opening develop at the centre of the top of the ankle. The inner and outer knee will feel parallel and the hips will be drawn down evenly towards the floor.

- The pelvis will begin to feel wider and more spaced. The curve at the back of the waist (the lumbar spine) will soften and slowly sink down into the floor, making a deeper contact each time you practise. As it lengthens the dilation in the centre of the back of the waist (between lumbar 3 and 4 vertebrae) will open. You may not feel this at first.

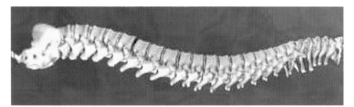

- Check the contact with the floor at the back of the head and the feet and develop a sense of balance. Exhale deeply and release the backs of the shoulders towards the floor, allowing the arms to open outwards and down, palms turned upwards towards the ceiling. Allow the shoulder blades to descend, flatten and widen along the floor. Notice how the base of the neck responds. Feel the spine sinking, lengthening and widening along the ground.

- Tune into your breathing and emphasise the exhalation. No force; just let all the breath go and at the end of the exhalation watch the inhalation come in naturally. Place all your attention in your breathing, allowing the breath out, and allowing it in, observing any pause developing between the two. Become interested in where the breath is going. Allow the incoming breath to find its own way without any interference from you. Notice how the body, maybe shyly at first, begins to follow the breath's lead. Observe what falls and what lifts as you gently and deeply exhale and inhale. Begin to be aware how the breathing is not a local event but a whole body involvement. Tune in to this. Notice the wave like rhythm unfolding. Simply enjoy what you are experiencing.

- When you feel rested, bend your knees to one side and roll over to bring yourself to a sitting position.

STAGE 2   Time: 20 minutes

Repeat **stage one** omitting the last 2 bullet points.

Anyone with HBP / heart problems should modify these instructions – release the arms to the floor horizontally not behind the head

- When the body has softened and a comfortable rhythm has established itself, raise the arms upward towards the ceiling, keeping the backs of the shoulders on the floor and inviting the weight to drop down through the arms into the floor. Exhaling, imagine the weight descending from the fingertips, through the wrists, elbow joints and shoulders; feel the pull of gravity drawing the weight out of the arms. There will be a sense of solidity at the base of the shoulders as the arms lighten. Sense the arms flowering up out of the ground. Imagine a favourite plant and observe how plants are rooted through the pull of gravity: they are held so that the opposing force can carry the stem upward towards the light. Find out if you can experience the arms feather-light, just be that uplifted experience, continuing to exhale the backs of the shoulders into the ground.

- Imagine the arms are on a ratchet, and with each subsequent exhalation let them fall back behind your head – gradually – to the floor. Check that your chin is close to your throat. Notice if the lumbar spine is lifting and, if it is, exhale deeply, inviting it to relax and drop back down into the floor. It may not comply, just observe what is happening.

- When your arms have completed their descent, hold one wrist and turn it away from you. Settle into your breathing pattern, emphasising the exhalation, discovering the extent of the inhalation and witnessing the pauses in between.

- Sense how the breathing pattern becomes circular, with the pauses linking the inhalation with the exhalation and vice versa.

- Slowly allow the arms to lift and bring them back to the floor, or sweep the arms back down by the sides of the body. Bend your knees to one side and come up to sitting.

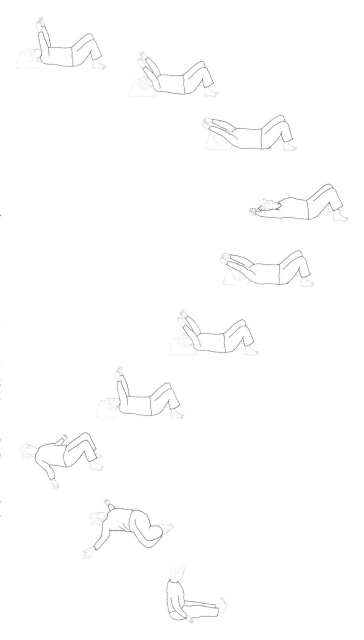

STAGE 3   Time: 20 minutes

As for **stage 2** omitting last bullet point

- Feel the back of the body connected with the floor. As you exhale release the weight to the pull of gravity, and on the inhalation feel the support coming back to you from the ground. Confirm this support as you settle into the deep exhalation and the free incoming breath.

- Notice the involuntary movements developing in the body as the spine releases itself along the ground. As you breathe pay particular attention to the exhalations.

- As you exhale, the tail bone and diaphragm separate out from each other, the tailbone moves towards the heels and the diaphragm is sucked back into the chest as it moves in the direction of the back of the head. As a consequence the lumbar spine feels longer.

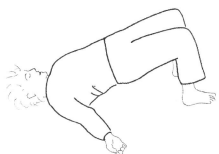

- As you exhale, the heels drop and the foot lengthens forwards. The weight is pulled strongly down. The feet begin to feel enormous.

- As you exhale, the ankles feel stronger, and this strength is carried through the legs.

- As you exhale, there is a sense of the body weight being drawn down towards the pelvis, down through the outer legs and releasing through the feet into the floor.

- As you exhale, and the weight is drawn down through the outer legs, there is a counter-pull up through the inner ankles and the inner thighs; and the pelvic floor is drawn in the same direction as the diaphragm travelling towards the back of the head.

- As the tailbone and pelvic floor pass each other on the exhalation, there is a slight movement upwards from the sacrum (the centre section of the pelvis that connects the tailbone with the lumbar spine). It feels like the beginnings of a pelvic tilt.

- All these involuntary movements are so subtle you have to pay full attention to them. As you tune in, begin to voluntarily join in the dance. Begin to augment the movement and incorporate your intention with the natural pattern and flow.

- Once you are comfortable and familiar with the directions of movement, exhale, releasing the feet and the shoulders into the floor, and invite the pelvis to float upwards. Follow the tailbone, the sacrum and the pull on the legs Maintain confidence in the strength of your feet, ankles and knees, and the pull on the backs of your shoulders. Just continue to breathe comfortably, imagining the inhalation as your power source (like fuel for your car) and then utilise this power (the exhalation), releasing the breath down the spine until the pelvis lifts like a plane, skywards.

- This takes time but once the pelvis learns how to float itself upward from the floor it will always be able to do it. If nothing seems to be happening and you become discouraged, give the pelvis a helping hand and consciously raise it slightly off the floor, being aware that you are employing muscles rather than the breath to achieve this. Then try floating the pelvis from there, releasing upwards on the exhalation, relaxing on the subsequent inhalation, and then floating upwards from where you left off on the next exhalation. Once you have the hang of it you will observe the very real difference between physically manoeuvring the body upwards and simply allowing the breath to float it upwards. The feeling will be softer, uncontrived and comfortable, and the feeling will be of being able to maintain the posture indefinitely. If you control it and maintain it with muscular effort you will inevitably feel a real need to let go and come back down. The difference is in the conservation and use of energy.

- Play with this, floating up and coming back down. See where the breath carries you – how you are at any one time will determine the quality of the posture.

- When you are ready to release down, imagine the individual vertebrae of the spine as beads on a string. Bring each bead down separately, sinking the back of the waist into the floor before releasing the pelvis.

- When you have finished playing, bend your knees to one side and roll up into a sitting position.

STAGE 4 Time: 20 minutes
Unsuitable for HBP / heart problems

As for **stage 3** omitting final instruction

- With the back of the body released back into the floor, incorporate the arm movements of **stage 2** with **stage 3** so that the arms begin to lift in tandem with the pelvis.

- As the back arches upwards, allow the arms to release back behind the head.

- Exhaling, feel the lengthening through the upper spine so that the curve in the upper back releases, and the spine between the shoulder blades feels as if it is moving in towards the back of the breastbone.

- Experience the strength in the legs, the toning in the pelvic floor, the softness at the back of the waist, the release in the shoulders, the lift in the chest as the collar bones widen, the comfortable pull at the back of the head and the ease through the neck.

- Notice the softness behind the eyes, the quiet brain, the sense of ease, tranquillity, peace pervading the entire physical structure.

- Release the body down on a long exhalation.

- Play with this and when you are ready, turn the legs to one side, and roll over to come up to sitting.

- Over time, your spine will ease, back problems that have developed through long held patterns of tension will ease or disappear and you will feel stronger mentally, emotionally and physically.

- These are the instructions. You have to practise them.

My CD: **"Wave Back"** would be complementary
to this practice and is available from www.abmworks.f9.co.uk

ALIGNING THE BODY FROM A SEATED POSITION   Time: 15 minutes

Correct posture allows your body to strengthen naturally. Back problems are endemic in our society today. Try this simple exercise. Not only will you feel taller, you'll lighten up.

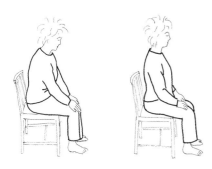

- Remove shoes, stockings, tights or socks.

- Sit on a comfortable high backed chair so that the feet are comfortably connected with the floor and you are not resting back into the chair back.

- Ensure that you are sitting on your sitting bones, the bones directly beneath your buttocks, not your sacrum, otherwise you will trap your spine and the idea is to release it.

- Notice exactly how you are sitting, whether your upper back is curved, whether you are slumped, whether your shoulders are relaxed or drooping, whether your head is level or bowed.

- Allow the feet to find the floor. Let them face forward and feel as if they are being pulled from below, across the ball of the foot and the centre of the base of the heel.

- Rest your hands comfortably in your lap.

- Have your chin drawn in, not down, and ensure you are looking straight ahead.

- Check your breathing and focus on breathing out. Exhale as much air as you comfortably can, and just wait for the in-breath to come in. Do not draw a breath in, just let it come to you and follow it until you feel the need to breathe out, then let it go completely.

- After a few breaths your breathing will have slowed to a comfortable rhythm.

- Now, as you continue to breathe in this pattern, allow your body weight to pass down through your pelvis, down your legs and through your feet into the floor on every exhalation.

- As the inhalation comes in allow your spine to begin to lengthen up out of the pelvis towards the back of your head. When you exhale do not slump, keep your spine steady, just let the weight go down.

- On every inhalation let your spine continue its ascent from where it left off, continuing to release the body weight down through the heavy pelvis and into the floor on the exhalation.

- As your spine straightens up towards the back of your head, you will feel longer, and comfortably grounded into the chair and the floor through your sitting bones and feet. Keep feeling the pull on your feet and allow the backs of the heels to roll down into the floor through the centre of the base of the heel.

- Just allow the spine to keep lengthening and relax your shoulders. Your neck should feel soft.

- Then, when you feel your body has naturally reorganised its posture, bring your attention to the tips of your shoulder blades. Invite them to draw down towards the back of your waist and feel them pulling on the backs of your shoulders.

- As the backs of the shoulders open and draw down towards the back of the waist, feel your collar bones (at the front) widen and the chest will lift.

- Feeling uplifted, breathe out and in a few times; then "float up" off your chair with your new body.

- Practise this for a few minutes every day and within a month you should be straightened out.

Remember: "Angels fly because they take themselves lightly." (Anon.)

ROTATING THE SPINE FROM A SEATED POSITION   Time: 10 minutes
Not recommended for diabetics / anyone with pancreatitis.

A lengthened spine loves to rotate, like a plant spiralling upwards. Rotation tones and strengthens the abdominal organs, especially the kidneys.

- Sit sideways on a high backed chair with your right shoulder closest to the chair back and your feet flat on the floor.

- Lengthen your spine according to the instructions above.

- When you feel fully and comfortably lengthened through your spine bring your attention in and **allow** the spine to rotate towards the right. Imagine a vine feeling its way upward around a central pole.

- As the spine rotates from the back of the waist upwards, the shoulders will turn. Allow the spiralling to continue up through the back of the neck, and let your head begin to turn.

- Take hold of the chair-back with your hands, the right hand to the side furthest away, and the left hand to the nearer one. This will stabilise you but be sure to hold the chair lightly, without grasping. **Allow** the chest to be drawn towards the chair-back without pulling.

  NB. *It is important to resist using the hands in such a way as to draw or impose movement on the rotating spine.*

  Breathe comfortably and on an exhalation allow your spine to unravel and bring you back to base position.

- Notice how you feel and then sit to the other side of the chair and repeat.

- When you return to base, observe how you are contacting the floor through your feet, the chair through your sitting bones. Observe the feelings and sensations in your trunk, abdomen and chest. Is the spine still elevated? Do you feel grounded through your base and uplifted?

Practising sitting on your sitting bones ensures the spine can lengthen. Many people sit on their sacrum and slump. Sitting on the sacrum deadens the sensations and sensitivity of the spine. Remember your spinal cord runs like a telephone cable the whole length of your spine, connecting with the brain.

"Sitting on a dead sacrum causes mental confusion higher up the spine"
John Stirk F.R.C.O (Osteopath and internationally renowned yoga teacher)

STANDING TALL

"Standing on our own two feet", "Standing up for ourselves",
"Taking a stand", "Standing our ground"......

- Stand with your feet a little apart and facing forwards. Keep your knees soft but not collapsed.

- Have the fronts of the feet at the big toe joints turned slightly in towards each other. If you have a lower back problem turn the fronts of the feet well in and ensure you maintain softness in the knees.

- Have a sense of standing over your feet, rather than back in your heel.

- Focus on your exhalation and allow the inhalation to come back to you, rather like dropping a rubber ball and collecting it back cleanly into your hand. The stronger the drop, the stronger the bounce back into the hand. Once the hand has collected the ball you absorb the texture, the feel of the ball through the palm of the hand, through the wrist and along the forearm, maybe into the elbow and beyond. In the same way, absorb the inhalation to the point where it seems to disappear. Then let go, completely. The more you give the breath away, the more fresh breath you get back. So just give it all away. Like love, it comes to you, it can be neither bought nor taken. The inhalation is a gift –from the Universe – freely given, to be freely accepted, used and given back again.

- Release the toes forwards and sense space between the toes and through each toe. Keep coming back to the breath without labouring it. Just softly let the breath go completely, and let it come back to you.

- Sense your foot on the ground. How is it contacting the floor? Where is the weight dropping? to the outside? inside? through the whole foot?

- Become aware of your whole foot, the heel, the outside edge, the ball of the foot, the toes, the big toe joint, the arch of the foot, the top of the foot.

- Mentally form a triangle with the centre of the base of the heel, the root of the little toe and the first big toe joint across the ball of the foot and have a sense of the foot being drawn down into the floor through those three points.

- Let the foot settle, let the weight drop evenly through the foot and, as the foot re-balances, you will sense the inner and outer ankles being balanced and feeling parallel; you may sense an opening at the top of the ankle.

- On the exhalations allow the body weight to descend through the pelvis, down the outer legs and into the floor through the pull on the feet.

- As the weight is drawn down into the floor the feet will develop confidence because the floor is their natural home; they belong with the floor. The knees will be pulled straight and the centre of the back of the knee will open. You will have a sense of the knees standing directly over your ankles, and the back of the heel rolling down, down into the floor through the centre of the base in the heel

- Keep allowing the weight to descend on the exhalation, letting the tailbone (between the sitting-bones) drop cleanly down towards the floor. The hips will realign over the knees and there will be a strong sense of the pull down the outer legs and a corresponding pull up on the inner legs. As the inner thighs draw up, the pelvic floor will lift upward, lending you a sense of strength and a feeling of integrity and support in the legs.

- As the legs realign, the spine can begin to release upwards out of the pelvis. Breathing out, keep allowing gravity to hold you through your feet, and on the in-breath feel the spine lengthening upwards away from the pelvis towards the back of the head. The lower back will begin to lengthen out and strengthen.

- Wherever the spine has reached by the end of the inhalation, just leave it there as you continue to exhale the body weight into the floor, and on the next inhalation allow the spine to continue its upward journey from where it left off. As the feet are pulled down by gravity, the anti-gravitational thrust from the ground travels up through the feet to the top of the head.

- There is a dilation at the centre of the lumbar spine, between lumbar 3 and 4 vertebrae, which allows the spine to lengthen simultaneously in two directions. As the weight is drawn down through the legs the upper body lightens and is released upwards.

- Sense the space developing at the back of the waist; around the chest; and as the spine continues to lift upwards towards the back of the head, the chest will lift, the collar bones will widen and the shoulders will relax down.

- Experience the enormous width – the broadening across the back of the shoulders and the upper back. As the spine continues its ascent, the upper back will lengthen out and the neck will release; and the head will re-balance on top of the spine, the chin will draw in towards the throat and you will be looking forwards.

- When the spine is fully released, and the legs maintain their integrity with the ground, you will feel lightness in the body, strength in the legs; you will feel inches taller and a sense of peace will pervade your entire body. You will feel assertive, confident and prepared for whatever life is bringing to meet you.

Practising standing tall develops self-confidence and alertness. It promotes a sense of well being.

It feels good!

A YOGA ROUTINE FOR THOSE WHO HAVE NO TIME TO PRACTICE YOGA

MORNING

1. On rising

- Sit on the edge of your bed with the feet flat on the floor, facing forwards.

- Rest your hands in your lap and allow your sitting bones to make contact with the edge of the bed.

- Exhaling, feel the body weight descending through the sitting bones down the legs and into the floor through the feet.

- Inhaling, allow the spine to begin its ascent gently out of the pelvis towards the back of the head.

- Paying attention to your breathing, exhaling down into the feet, receiving the inhalation to let the upper body lift, allow your back to straighten up.

NB Anyone with HBP / heart problems ignore the next 2 instructions:

- When the body feels light, and the seat grounded through the sitting bones into the bed, let your arms float up above your head. They should feel light. If they feel heavy, bring them down, allow the spine to lengthen a little more, feel the weight in your pelvis and try again. When you feel comfortable, hold one wrist and turn it up towards the ceiling as you gently exhale and inhale a few times.

- Yawn, and let the breath go on a heavy sigh. Float the arms back again and stand up.

- Drink a glass of warm water (optional) and enjoy your day.

2. A Bathroom routine

- If your washbasin has a pedestal, stand with your hands shoulder-width apart holding the edge of the washbasin.

- Walk the legs back until the arms are horizontal and you can place your head between your arms. Then walk the legs back so that the feet are directly under the hips and the arms remain straight.

- On an exhalation allow the tailbone to feel heavy and draw away from the body. Let the tailbone slowly extend the spine as you exhale. When you feel the spine has lengthened out, bend the knees, step forward and come up to standing.

- Allow the weight to drop through your feet and let the spine lengthen upward towards the back of your head.

- Alternatively, stand facing the wall with your fingertips touching the wall at the height of your hips. As you walk back, allow the palms to come down until they make full contact with the wall. Then proceed as above.

If you have an arched upper back, take your arms higher up the wall, and with the palms flat against the wall, walk back until they are straight. Bring the feet back until they are underneath the hips, and allow the spine to lengthen out as instructed above.

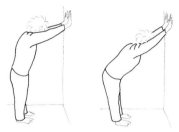

If the bedroom or bathroom does not appeal, the kitchen makes a good substitute. You can lengthen the spine against the kitchen sink waiting for the kettle to boil,

Or you can use a chair to awaken your spine as you are about to start your breakfast.

Failing that you can wait until you reach the office and as you adjust your chair, you can practise the exercise there instead.

Choose one or more of these postures to revitalise your spine. Remember to allow the posture to develop out of the exhalation. No force or strain.

EVENING

- Lie full length on the floor on your front. Prop your chin in your hands and relax with your legs slightly separated, toes turned in towards each other and heels out. Feel the belly being softly drawn down into the floor, feel the support of the hips and the upper legs (front of thighs). This can be a very comfortable position from which to watch the television. Just ensure you are a comfortable distance away for your eyes to focus without strain. I read the paper, magazines and even novels in this position. It is a pose that comes naturally to small children and teenagers and there is no need to relinquish it when we become adults or pensioners!

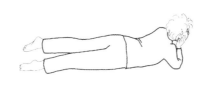

- With your legs apart and feet flat on the floor facing forwards, sit on your sitting bones on the edge of a chair or bed. Ensure your feet are flat on the floor, facing forwards. Allow the weight to fall and your spine to lengthen. Tuck your fingers into the top of your hips, feeling the crease deepen.

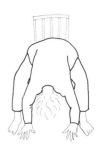

- Then, with your chin rolling down towards your throat, fold your body over your legs and roll down towards the floor between your knees. Release your hands towards the floor; if they reach the floor, turn the backs of the wrists over so that the backs of the hands contact the floor. Keep your neck soft with the chin rolled in towards the throat, and keep your sitting bones in contact with the chair or bed at all times. Just enjoy the tranquillity of the breath flowing in and flowing out as you follow the rhythm.

- When you are ready to come up, feel as if your tail bone is being drawn down towards the floor and come up from there with a soft straight back. If you have a sore back or a back problem just roll yourself up, keeping your chin rolled down towards your throat until the base of your neck feels ready to straighten. **NB. If you have HBP / heart problems do not take your head below your heart when forward bending.**

YOGA FOR LIFE

This routine has been devised around three points of the day: morning, mid-morning and evening.

The idea is to select what is appropriate for you at a time of day to suit you, and to improvise and adapt the exercises into your everyday routine.

All movement needs to be based on the principles outlined below:

At no time should a movement be forced. Allow the posture to unfold and develop from the involuntary movements that you sense within your body as you rest and breathe. The involuntary movements, once engaged through your senses, can then be augmented through your will. In other words, you begin to join in what is essentially the body reflecting the cosmic dance in its eternal 3-fold pattern of contraction, rest and expansion at the different frequencies we call vibration.

The various routines allow for postures to link serially. Just enjoy what is comfortable for you at the time you are practising, and wait for development to come to you.

In the morning, after a good night's sleep, my spine is rested and at its most flexible. This is the time when my body loves to back bend, the time it is most joyous in The Wheel ...

.....but not necessarily every day. Some days it is happiest in The Cobra,

......and some days it wants to stay with just floating the pelvis.

If I am practising mid-morning I sometimes simply lie in semi-supine

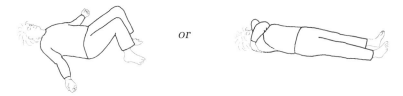

or

or with my arms folded in a hug over my chest and just breathe. It looks as if I am doing nothing, but in listening to my breath, staying with it, paying complete attention, I am receiving a very valuable education. I have known the luxury of being in this position, without knowing over an hour has passed by until I have rolled over, and come back to sitting.

This is meditation and, to paraphrase Krishnamurti, it rescues us from the tyranny of ideas and beliefs that we have about the world, and teaches us how to experience directly.

This brings enormous benefits that can only be felt, not explained.

"To discover Truth we need to make the heart white through meditation rather than black with religious composition or the air thick with learned conversation" (Source unknown)

MORNING

EVENING

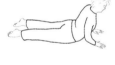

The human diet from the historical perspective based on the philosophy of Rudolph Steiner

- Nutritional customs have altered over aeons of time.

- Human consciousness **is evolving**. We have not always related to the world with the same degree of consciousness

- Food not only sustains us on a physical level, it plays a part in altering or expanding human consciousness. (cf. Mind and mood altering substances such as recreational drugs, magic mushrooms, tobacco and alcohol.)

- **Anthroposophy** (spiritual science) teaches that the human purpose is to re-spiritualise or transubstantiate matter.

In the early 1980s Rupert Sheldrake, a plant physiologist, demonstrated that the morphogenetic field exists **prior** to the formation of matter. He validated the existence of this non-material blueprint, or the specific electro-magnetic field from which all organisms materialise according to their particular map or plan. What he was saying is the spirit has a body whereas we tend to think of bodies with a spirit. This proof upset the modern scientific world at the time but made perfect sense to anthroposophists. Darwin and Steiner's findings do not so much conflict as describe evolution from opposite ends of the pole: the one was a materialist looking up, the other an anthroposophist looking down, the telescope.

Much earlier, in the previous century, Rudolph Steiner had asserted that "the human spirit gradually lays hold on itself and on the world. Since foods are part of the world, it lays hold on these too, and in digesting learns to digest the world."[1] In other words *how we learn* is influenced by how we digest what we physically eat. Gradually we are beginning to understand that poor concentration and mental assimilation as well as hyperactivity in children is largely down to a defective diet of junk food and foods laced with additives.

From the anthroposophical perspective digestion proper takes place in the centre of the organism under the influence of the solar plexus. Yoga has always referred to this area as our internal sun, and mystics have always called it the fire centre. Orthodox science concedes that this area of the human anatomy concerns itself with physical digestion, and that physical digestion has an effect on our emotional and mental states. When we eat too much last thing at night we cannot sleep; when we are upset we cannot eat. We also speak of digestion in abstract terms when we are "fired up with enthusiasm", or when someone has an idea to share s/he is told to "fire away". Depression and poor appetite often go hand in hand. When describing someone "out of spirits" we say s/he has no appetite for life. So on some level we all know the validity of these findings, our ancestral heritage is carried in the language. Food is commonplace as metaphor in the most mundane conversation.

HUMAN CONSCIOUSNESS
as three separate stages of
the human's development

Moon, Sun and Earth
Components

1. THE MOON STAGE.

The Primary Phase equating with early human development and group consciousness.

This phase pre-dates the Vedas, the earliest recorded philosophical texts. During this period humans had developed no intellectual capacity whatsoever but possessed the power to perceive a world beyond the senses. In those times the spiritual world was as real as our physical surrounds are to us. In fact it was more real because the natural world was perceived as Maya or Illusion, considered the lowest phase of creation. Yoga still teaches this concept. Those of a religious disposition believe in a "life" after physical death and many others of no religious persuasion or affiliation admit to feelings of "something other" than what they can sense. So, to one degree or another, a sense of the ethereal remains embodied in the human.

Our early ancestors were not self-conscious but felt wholly at one with the gods, each being an instrument through which the divine pulsated – rather like the operation of the bee colony. Personal freedom was not an option, individual judgments and decisions impossible. They were in the lap of the gods and their personalities would have been childlike and undeveloped.

Our planet is part of the Milky Way.

Spiritual science (anthroposophy) reports that at one time, *when the earth and moon were a single entity,* the moon principle permeated the planet. Earth's atmosphere was suffused with a milky, egg-white like substance which living creatures absorbed as food.

Only much, much later, after the moon had separated from Earth, did organs of lactation form inside an animal body as part of a reproduction system. Milk is a complete food, a liquid synthesis of fat, protein, carbohydrate and mineral salts. Hauschka points out that all the building materials of the animal, vegetable and mineral kingdoms are contained in milk as though in embryo.

Milk is connected with the moon principle. It is the product of living, sentient animals whose organs of lactation are part of the reproductive system and reproduction is subject to the MOON rhythms (the menses).

Milk and milk products were the earliest forms of nourishment, and the chief food of this period of evolution. Animals were raised for their milk. Remnants of this practice can still be found today amongst certain nomadic tribes. The Masai include the blood and milk of their cattle in their diet. And cattle, sacred to this day for Hindus, have always played an important role in Indian mythology.

2. THE SUN STAGE

The Secondary Phase equating with Zarathustra and the Persian Civilisation and the development of the individual (ego).

This was when humanity experienced an awakening interest in Earth and Nature. Zarathustra taught the cultivation of plants that are, to date, still our most important source of food. Fruits and grains grown today all spring from the rose and lily families and up until fairly recently there have been essentially no new plant-breeding developments. The Zend Avesta compiled by Zarathustra can claim to be the first agricultural text book and under his guidance the Persians began a rudimentary agriculture. Fruits and vegetables replaced milk as the main form of nutrition. So food in the main came to be a SUN product since plants are under the operational guidance of the sun.

The plant, representing the second or middle phase of human development, occupies a middle position between animal and mineral in another sense too. The root, at its base, is salty and bitter and lives within the mineral earth, while its opposite end, the blossom where it develops sweet nectars and juicy fruits, is connected with animate insects.

Hauschka takes the nutritional dimension even further by reminding us it was the parts above the ground we used first. When conceptualising an ideal state we talk about a Land of Milk and Honey, and inasmuch as we first ate the sweetest part of plants, honey can be equated with the fruits of plants. We used roots later which, Hauschka claims formed a bridge over to the mineral phase. We mineralise sugar through cooking and refining, and beet sugar is actually derived from the root not the stem of the plant.

Hence, the Sun-plant connection led to the development of the individual ego, leading us away from a group consciousness into the rudiments of an individual one.

By the time of the Egyptians, the priest-kings were still capable of clairvoyance but this was ebbing even for the Greek Initiates. There is no absolute cut-off point between the stages of evolution. Rather, a blending so that each progressive stage of evolution incorporates the previous stages. We still retain the intuitive powers of our earliest ancestors, which can be developed, but for the most part clairvoyant and clairaudient powers are limited today to a minority of sensitives within society.

Hauschka relates in his book, *"Nutrition"*, how mythology demonstrates our evolutionary history through the Cain and Abel story. Abel, the shepherd, belongs to phase one and is pleasing to God. Cain, the farmer (and not quite so close to God), has a mind of his own, which is subject to error. When his sacrifice is rejected by the Almighty he slays his brother. According to Hauschka, death and killing – metaphorically linked with becoming separated from God and developing an independent ego - symbolises the new, progressive state of consciousness over-riding an old, outworn condition. Guilt and error was the price our developing ego paid for it.

Earth's larder and human life are inextricably intertwined and as we evolve so does the food we consume. Historically we set out as hunter-gatherers. Harnessing our food supply was our first step towards civilisation. Agriculture took us away from a predominantly animal existence and, for the first time, gave us a future. Consciously having a future allowed the human to plan, which led him out of a predominantly-unconscious present. Agriculture was a giant leap forwards for the human and his/her expanding consciousness. The seeds were sown, literally.

3. THE EARTH STAGE

The Third Phase: The Modern Period – equating with the Roman Civilisation; the development of the intellect, to where we stand today.

The term "mineral" is denoted in its widest context.

As civilised peoples began to crave mineral salts in food, so another element is introduced. During this phase human nutrition takes on its EARTH characteristic. When humans moved away from using animal products (milk) and began killing them and eating them, using a variety of cooking techniques and recipes (reducing the food by boiling, roasting and SALTING) the tendency is towards a deadening, mineralising direction.

The human intellect has developed out of the third phase to such a point that we have become increasingly free of the spiritual world and of spiritual guidance. Minerals, rooted in the plant, nourish the human intellect which is rooted in the head. Minerals are brain food and, as Colbin astutely observes, it is interesting that children, at the stage where they are about to talk, show a tendency for carrots.

Intellectualism and materialism go hand in hand. The "terrible twos" is that stage of development where the toddler has come to differentiate between mine and yours, which usually means mine and mine until s/he is taught differently!

Greek philosophy entered the phase of logical conceptual thinking with Aristotle and the mind-body split has also been linked with this stage of human development. Over the centuries we have developed modern abstract thinking which is represented in both modern literature and art. Copernicus still believed the universe to be a living organism but this notion became quaint to those living after him. Newton and Descartes led us to mechanism which served as a framework for all our scientific thinking up until Einstein and his theory of Relativity, and the Quantum physicists.

Yoga is a philosophy that pre-dates religion. However, yoga, as it is currently understood and practised in the West, derives from a tradition codified in the Indian sub-continent only some 5000 years ago. This practice takes many forms but its single goal is to lead the practitioner to self-realisation. In a much broader context yoga stands for Universal Truth and is, therefore, both timeless and ubiquitous. It is form and formlessness both or, as modern physics attests, the particle and the wave.

It is said that the entire span of human history can be seen through the stages of a single human life. As babies we experience the world directly: we believe what we see, hear and touch and we are present, though this presence is largely unconscious. This would equate with phase one. At some point in this life-span our consciousness splits (phase two) and with this development we begin to experience the world indirectly inasmuch as we come to see, hear and feel what we believe. Intellectual thought develops individual opinion, which develops into belief and we express points of view. And, as Anna explains – in that most delightful book *"Mister God, this is Anna"* – the vital difference between us and God lies in the fact that we have points *of* view whereas "Mister God has points *to* view"[3]

During phase two we are experiencing the world in duality. We speak of the body (form) and the mind (the formless) and, through yoga practice, attempt to merge the two parts of us into one whole when, actually, there is nothing to do. We are already both; we simply have to realise this, consciously. Whether we engage in traditional yoga practice, or not is irrelevant – to live fully we have to realise this fundamental wholeness consciously. We have to go beyond the concept that we arose out of the merging of a single egg and a single sperm and realise that actually we arose out of Consciousness itself. The idea or blueprint of the human manifested out of the whole creative process and the "Idea of the human" preceded the "Fact of the human". The idea always precedes the result whether it is a human or a fruit cake!

Today we stand at a threshold, as did our ancestors prior to unfolding onto another dimension of consciousness. Much is made of a New Age, the dawning of Aquarius and a giant leap forward. The nutritional tendency at the moment is still towards further descent into the hardening realms of death forces, along a route of technological manipulation (junk foods, synthetics, and drugs) which takes us away from beings into the realms of machines.

On the other hand the whole subject of nutrition has never featured so large in our consciousness. Be it healthy eating, junk diets, fad diets, vegetarianism, GM technology or organic farming, one way or another we are obsessed with food. And this is largely due to technological advances – without the mass media the debate would be local rather than global.

In another direction a sense of our spirituality is all around us and is pervasive. There is emphasis on personal development and self-realisation. We are encouraged to take personal responsibility for our decisions and our lives. Whilst there is a heightened sense of individualism there is also a deeper sense of belonging to something bigger than the individual self be it an other, a family or the environment. Increasingly there is a sense of an internal as opposed to an external God. In Yoga this equates with the Atman.

Today we all have choices that were denied our forebears. We are more intellectually aware of, and more scientifically knowledgeable about, our environment than our ancestors were. Human consciousness has expanded to the point of being able to make *concrete* choices from moment to moment, and that consciousness is expanding at breathtaking speed. We have developed the means to carry us physically beyond the confines of this planet and we are beginning to appreciate our inextricable links with Mother Earth. We are starting to care for her as never before because we realise we are part and parcel of her. Slowly we are realising that we and our planet are one.

In the yoga tradition we move from a point to come back to a point. Life in all its dimensions spirals. Maybe we are poised to rediscovering the world as a living entity, to *realising* that the whole planet breathes, and that its entire history is recorded in and by the human being. In other words it is only through human consciousness that our Universe is made self-conscious. Without us having come this far the Big Bang would still be unrecorded and un-reflected somewhere out in the ether. That we have arrived at this point in Consciousness has everything to do with when, where, how and what we eat.

[1] Rudolph Hauschka *"Nutrition"* Steiner Press Chapter 3 Page 18

[2] Hauschka *"Nutrition"* fig.8 page 79

[3] *"Mister God, This is Anna"* Fynn.

RECIPE INDEX

REFERENCES

The Complete Book of Herbs and Spices	Clare Loewenfeld &Philippa Back	Published by David and Charles
Crime & Diet	Michio Kushi	JapanPublications Inc.
Crime Diet and Delinquency	Alexander Schauss.	
The Diary of a Farmer's Wife 1796–1797	Anne Hughes	Penguin
Diet and Nutrition	Rudolph Ballantine M.D.	Himalayan Int.Institute
The Dynamics of Nutrition	Gerhard Schmidt M.D.	Biodynamic Literature
Flowers to the Rescue	Gregory Vlamis	Thorsons
Food and Healing	Anne-Marie Colbin	Ballantine Books
Light, Medicine of the Future	Jacob Liebermann	Bear & Co.
The Macrobiotic Diet	Aveline & Mischio Kushi	
Mister God This Is Anna	Fynn	Fount Paperbacks
The Natural Food Catalogue	Vikki Peterson	Macdonald & Jane 1978
The Nature of Substance	Rudolph Hauschka	Steiner Press
Nutrition	Rudolph Hauschka	Steiner Press
Nutrition & Agriculture	Dr. Kolisko	Published in *"Anthroposophical Agricultural Foundation"* Vol. 4 No. 7. December 1936. Reprinted 1982. Copyright 1982 by A. Clunies-Ross
The Science & Art of Healing	Ralph Twentyman	Floris Books
Sub-Nature and Supernature	Dr. Ehrenfried Pfeiffer	Mercury Press
Thought As a System	David Bohm	Routledge
The Turning Point	Fritjof Capra	Flamingo
Vibrational Medicine	Richard Gerber M.D.	Bear & Co.